$3.50

P9-CRI-852

THREE RIVER SOUTH:

A Story of Young Abe Lincoln

By VIRGINIA S. EIFERT

Illustrated by THOMAS HART BENTON

IN THE SPRING of 1831, after the Lincoln family had survived the Winter of the Deep Snow, young Abe Lincoln was more than willing to accept an offer to pilot a flatboat full of produce down three rivers of middle America, from Sangamo Town to the roaring city of New Orleans. Although others went along, it was Abe Lincoln who planned everything, made the important decisions and avoided danger or fought it down all along the way.

Virginia Eifert, the author, lives in Springfield, Illinois, Abraham Lincoln's home town. She herself has followed the course of young Abe along the Sangamon, the Illinois and the mighty Mississippi—*Three Rivers South*—and knows the background of his trip. Against this she has dramatized one unforgettable adventure after another, each bringing out the character of the great and beloved American in the light of his future principle achievements. There was the building of the flatboat, mostly by stalwart Abe, when the logs along the river bank were worn smooth by the men and boys who gathered on them daily to watch and to listen to Abe's tales, laugh at his jokes, and finally pitch in to help. Abe's warm friendship with two gracious, elderly Southern gentlewomen contrasts with his facing up to the ruthless river pirates. There was the time, too, when Abe gave refuge to a runaway slave, only to have him turn up again with his family on the slave block in New Orleans. Abe's solution of that provided a rewarding climax to his trip. And all along, of course, there was the fascination, beauty and threat of river travel, all of which Abe Lincoln handled in his own right way.

Thomas Hart Benton, distinguished American artist, has made this a stunning book with his thirteen full-page pictures, done in wash and line.

An ageless book.

DODD, MEAD & COMPANY

THREE RIVERS SOUTH

A Story of Young Abe Lincoln

YOUNG ABE LINCOLN

THREE RIVERS SOUTH

A Story of Young Abe Lincoln

BY

VIRGINIA S. EIFERT

ILLUSTRATED BY THOMAS HART BENTON

DODD, MEAD & COMPANY · NEW YORK · 1959

Library of Congress Catalog Card Number: 53-7784
Printed in the United States of America
by Vail-Ballou Press, Inc., Binghamton, N. Y.
Designed by Stefan Salter

FOR LARRY

The general situation and many of the events described in this book are based upon historical facts. However, the fictional characters are wholly imaginative: they do not portray and are not intended to portray any actual persons.

ILLUSTRATIONS

THREE RIVERS SOUTH

A Story of Young Abe Lincoln

CHAPTER ONE

On a raw gray day in March, 1831, Abe Lincoln, in the bow of a heavy cottonwood canoe, bent strongly to his paddle. Cousin John Hanks worked the stern paddle. Jack Johnston, Abe's step-brother, in the middle of the canoe, held onto the sides and hoped the river water wouldn't stain his good hat, which just then had been well doused when John caught a snag and splashed them all.

But Abe wouldn't have minded getting soaked to the skin, not when he had ahead of him the prospect of a long journey down three rivers in the spring of the year. It was the year when Abe Lincoln was twenty-two, and with the exception of one other river trip to New Orleans when he was nineteen, he had never gone anywhere, had never done anything that could equal the prospects of this coming adventure.

The heavy cottonwood canoe wallowed around the bends and galloped down the straightaway. The three navigators pulled up at Jamestown, whose landing was awash in the high water, and there they sold the canoe to a riverman. They set out on foot across the seven muddy miles to Springfield, on the Illinois prairie. And young Abe Lincoln, slogging through the gumbo, couldn't remember when a springtime had meant more to him.

For adventure lay waiting in Springfield, adventure and a chance to see the world. Well, part of it, anyway.

"Think Mr. Offutt'll have his boat all ready to go, soon as we get there?" asked John Hanks, who was lean and dark, with the long, narrow Hanks face and unsmiling gray eyes. "If he hasn't, the flood crest'll pass and it'll be too late to go." And John privately hoped that it would. He was married and had a family, and already he was sorry he had gone off on this junket with young Abe and Jack.

"When he hired us to take him to New Orleans," remarked Abe, sloshing through the mud, "he said he'd have all his barrels and live hogs ready to load on as big a flatboat as he could buy. Mr. Offutt's an important man around here and he gets things done. He said so himself," added Abe, although he had begun to have certain vague misgivings as soon as the important Mr. Denton Offutt, departing from the bleak Lincoln cabin on the Decatur prairie, had ridden away on his bony horse across the thawing sod.

"Sure hope so!" remarked Jack with enthusiasm, making a new trail for himself through the bent-over, soggy prairie grasses, which at least made a better foothold than the bottomless black mud. Jack hated to get mud on his boots. "Be a downright shame to miss this here trip." Jack Johnston had been hardly anywhere in his life, except in backwoods Indiana and Kentucky and now in Illinois. Abe's own enthusiasm had filled Jack with an eagerness to ride three rivers down to see the great city of New Orleans. All during the past long winter, Abe had never stopped talking about that trip of his three years before, with Allen Gentry on a flatboat.

Finally the three sloshed down the muddy main street of Springfield, with its ramshackle board shanties and lean and scraggy horses tied to the hitching rails. A huge, mud-crusted sow lay on her side in the street while her little pigs suckled. Another sow challenged the three young men as they approached, and her red eyes gleamed wickedly. Abe, Jack, and John stepped nimbly out of her way and went up to the porch of a grocery store.

"Where's the Buckhorn Tavern, sir?" Abe asked the first man he saw. Jack kicked out at a thin yellow dog which snapped at his ankles, and mud from his boot flew in the dog's face and stopped its yapping for a moment or two. He hated animals, especially dogs, which seemed to sense his dislike and always chose him to bark at or snap at. Jack hated most things with four legs. Abe could not forget how his stepbrother, when he was a boy, had smashed the shell of a box turtle and then watched the creature struggle until it died.

The man whom Abe addressed never lifted his eyes from his job of scraping gumbo off his boots.

"Down yon'," he said languidly, picking up a buggy whip and pointing with it up the street before giving the yellow dog a lick with the lash.

"Mr. Offutt told me he'd be at the Buckhorn Tavern for sure. Said he was almost always there, or else Mr. Elliott could tell us where to find him," Abe explained, and hoped he'd have no trouble in locating the jolly, talkative little man who had promised so much that day when the snow still lay on the prairie near Decatur. The Winter of the Deep Snow had been enough to gall any man into action. After those terrible months of bitter cold and the blowing white smother of snow—cold and snow for months on end—activity was a relief and a satisfaction. Thirteen people in a two-room cabin—Halls, Hankses, and Lincolns, newly come from Indiana—had struggled with the problems of not enough food, not enough warmth, cramped living and sleeping quarters, and dispositions which, in that long confinement, clashed until they all hated each other. Wind blew icily through all the cracks. The drifts piled higher. An icy crust had formed on the great snowbanks, so that wolves could sneak out and snatch deer which were floundering because they couldn't stand up. The wolves had caught the wild turkeys, too. For hours on end the wind had raved out of the north and had blown snow splinters into Abe's face until they brought the blood. On those days of unending cold, he had gone out to cut a thousand fence rails for William Warnick and had nearly frozen his feet. If Sally Warnick hadn't rubbed them with rabbit oil, he'd likely not have any feet now, Abe remembered, with a grimace at how they had hurt. And so when winter was finally nearing its end, stout little Mr. Offutt of Springfield had come along and had offered Abe a job piloting a flatboat of produce down to the Queen City of New Orleans. The pay was only ten dollars a month, but the chance to get away and see the world—that was worth everything. So Abe had persuaded his stepmother's son, Jack, who had grown up with him as a brother, to come along. Sandy-haired, unambitious young Jack had been easy to persuade; he'd never had much gumption to do things on his own. The sour-visaged John Hanks hadn't been so easy, yet finally he had reluctantly agreed. And now, joyfully, Abe could almost feel the deck of the big flatboat pitching and sliding over the rough waters of the Mississippi, could even now almost smell New Orleans.

No, that smell which met his nostrils was just Andrew Elliott's Buckhorn Tavern!

While the other two leaned on the hitching rail outside the

FOOT ON THE LOG, WIND IN HIS HAIR, BIG HANDS WAVING THE MALLET FOR
EMPHASIS, ABE'D GO ON FOR TWENTY MINUTES FROM MEMORY

IN THE SURGING, BOILING, WHIRLING CURRENT OF THE FLOODING SANGA-
MON, THE CANOE WAS AT THE MERCY OF THE TOSSING BROWN WATER . . .

tavern door, Abe went in. When his eyes grew used to the gloom, he spotted the stout figure of Mr. Denton Offutt, just raising his glass for one more.

"Mr. Offutt," said Abe, easy-like. Denton Offutt set down his glass with a thump and peered blearily in the direction of the voice. Abe walked over to the table.

"It's me, Mr. Offutt, Abe Lincoln. I've come to pilot your flatboat, remember?" Then as Offutt still gaped blankly, Abe hastened to add, while his heart sank, "You recollect you hired me and John Hanks and Jack Johnston over near Decatur—well, we're ready and the Sangamon's flooding high!"

"Sure, sure, I recollect!" Offutt laughed gaily. " 'Nother whiskey, Andy," he called to the owner of the tavern. "Sure I do. Good ol' Denton Offutt don't forget a face. Abe Lincoln it is, but *ho-ho-ho*, you'll laugh when you hear the joke—Andy, come over here and listen, this is the best joke of the season. Look, I hired this here Lincoln feller to take my pork and corn down to N' Orleans and here he is, big as life and twice as natural—" He roared with laughter and promptly toppled off his chair.

Soberly, Abe helped him to his seat.

"And ye know what?" Offutt giggled. "There ain't no boat! I plumb forgot to get me one!" He pounded happily on the stained table. "I got me three fine rivermen, and no boat!" And he rolled off his chair again and lay laughing up at them from the littered, dusty floor.

Abe let him lie. Inside himself he felt sick and at the same time boiling mad. At that dismal moment the splendid city of New Orleans seemed a million miles away. Outside the tavern, Jack and John shifted uneasily from foot to foot and wondered what was happening in there. A raw March wind blew cold out of the north.

"Might even snow again," said John Hanks morosely. "Let's go inside. No use in us freezin' out here while Abe takes his time in there."

They opened the door and stepped into the tavern just in time to see Abe bend his lanky length and with a single swoop yank Mr. Offutt to his feet. The little man stopped his silly laughing and hiccupped. Tears ran down his blotchy fat cheeks. To John Hanks and Jack Johnston, it was an unbelievable sight—their usually mild-mannered kinsman actually was shaking their employer! Abe Lincoln hardly ever lost his temper.

"D-don't you sh-shake me like that, young f-feller," babbled Mr. Offutt.

"Listen," said Abe grimly, still shaking the little man and towering in a fury above him. Abe's bony hands gripped the plump shoulders.

"Listen to me. Stop that infernal giggling and listen or I'll shake it out of you. We'll build you a boat. Do you hear what I say—*we'll build you a boat!* We can get the lumber along the river and build you a proper boat before the flood goes. Only we got to work fast." He shook Offutt again. "Where's a mill that can cut us some planks?" Abe demanded.

"S-Sangamo Town," stuttered Offutt, goggling at the thin, furious face above him. "Plenty good timber—gov'ment lands. Sawmill, too."

"Fine," said Abe, letting go, and Offutt slumped weakly into his chair. Abe felt a wonderful surge of power. It was the first time he could remember when he had stood up like a man and had told another man off—when he'd really stood up to better himself. It was a good feeling. Even if he had to do it with his bare hands, they'd have a boat after all.

"Fine!" he repeated, beaming. "Tomorrow you take us there. I've got no money to pay the mill. You got to attend to that. I'll do the rest!"

CHAPTER TWO

ACROSS THE hills covered with weathered, copper-colored, turkey-foot grass, the good south sun came shining on the houses of Sangamo Town. On the north, the forest kept off the cold winds, and now in March it seemed as if spring really had begun to come to the country along the Sangamon. Certainly the village on its high hill above the river was prettier than muddy, ugly Springfield down there on the prairie, Abe thought, as he climbed the south slope. At least here you didn't have to shove the hogs out of the way before you could step onto the board sidewalk of the business houses, and there was indeed a fine air of clatter and bustle with the carding mill in operation. This was a promising little place, for all it had been laid out only seven years before. Even so, it was bigger than Springfield, almost as big as Chicago which, in the year 1831, had 250 persons living in it.

The streets were laid out neatly in the clearing on top of the tall hill above the winding, swirling Sangamon. A wagon road went down the hill and crossed the river at Roll's Ford, where a layer of blackish limestone made a good solid footing for men and wagons. The muddy, treacherous Sangamon was not always so obliging. Not far away from the ford, along the heavily forested shore, stood a sawmill. It was near here that Abe would build the flatboat for Mr. Offutt. Now that matters were well in hand, Denton Offutt had gone back to Springfield, promising to return in a few weeks.

Abe's heart swelled with pride when he thought of that flatboat. He could hardly wait to get started, but there was something else that had to be done first.

"First we've got to build a shanty for shelter," said Abe. Jack, John and Abe threw it together fast—they would be in it only a few weeks, and it needn't be fancy. Abe was elected cook, and the meals weren't fancy, either. Abe Lincoln never had had much experience with anything but plain cabin food, and that was what they had here. It was mostly corn pone, fried pork, and hominy; catfish if one of the boys caught a mess in the river, greens if Abe happened to see some—poke greens just sprouting through old leaves in the woods, dandelions around the village, wild lettuce, maybe, or sour dock.

"Eat up, now," ordered Abe in a "motherly" way. "These greens'll thin your blood, and land only knows it ought to be plenty thick after all that corn pone and pork all winter!"

Up in the village on the hill, folks enjoyed Abe's company. There was something about this Abe Lincoln, something which glowed in his face when he talked, that pulled them to him. And there were his stories: he was always good at stories. Abe liked visiting and he especially liked being invited to Caleb Carman's dinner table where the food was good and the conversation was more than just crop talk and complaining about the president, the weather, and the roads.

For the first time in his life since he had learned to read, Abe Lincoln was without a book. There were few in the homes of the villagers, and newspapers were rarely seen, especially during the mud-time when a horse couldn't pull through it and even men got discouraged and quit. So if he couldn't read, Abe talked. He had always liked to talk, and all last winter when the thirteen of them were cramped in that cabin on the Decatur prairie, it had been the words he spoke and the stories he told which perhaps saved their reason.

Caleb Carman was a stout gentleman with piercing blue eyes and a glistening bald head. He had made sneering remarks about the "passel of greenhorns come up from Springfield," but although he may have kept his opinion about the two others, he changed it about Abe after hearing him tell a good story at the hitching rail.

"Many bears around here?" Abe had asked a slouching fellow who was cutting off a new chaw of plug.

"Naw, not so many," the lounger replied, working his jaws around the fresh quid. "All shot off."

"Well, now," said Abe conversationally, "there was a time over in Indiana when the bears were so thick you couldn't leave a plug of dog-leg out on the wash bench without a black bear coming up and taking it, even in broad daylight. I mind there was a time a fellow down the road a piece came tearing up and yelling, 'Abe, Abe, get your gun and come quick! I got me a bear treed down to my place!'

" 'Well, now, Tom,' I told him, 'that bear'd be gone time we got there.'

" 'No, he won't,' Tom yelled at me. 'Get your gun and come fast. The bear'll stay. Maw's down below with the pitchfork!' and that's what she was. Old Mis Tyler was a hatchet-faced woman, if there ever was one, ugly enough, I'll swear, to scare off even a bear. And there she was down below that bear with her pitchfork ready, and the bear with a sour look was hanging on up in the tree a way. Tom was too shaky to fire, so I did it for him, and the bear came down with a thump, dead. I reckon, for a fact, that was the first and last bear I ever shot." Abe looked soberly around at his audience.

"Well, sir," he went on solemnly, his eyes twinkling over at Caleb Carman who had joined the group. "Old Mis Tyler just gave that bear a look, and stomped without a word back into the house. No shoes on, of course, 'twas still warm weather. But she was so mad being kept so long underneath that tree that she stomped up to the porch and when she saw a shoat standing in the doorway just heading into the house, she got in behind that pig and gave it a kick that popped her big toe joint loud as a pistol-shot, so help me!" And Abe grinned as the men roared. They slapped their legs and 'lowed that was a good one.

But Abe didn't spend very much of his time enjoying himself in the village. Down in the bottoms there was work to be done and it started immediately. The three builders rafted logs out of the government land and had them cut into heavy planks at the mill. Then they set to work to build a flatboat. But while Abe laid out the shape of the boat and hammered the wooden pegs which held it together, he talked. The old sycamores in the river bottoms along the boiling brown Sangamon never before nor since had heard such talk.

Lured by the excitement of the project, the fellows of the town began straggling down the hill soon after the sun was up and breakfast was over. As the mists steamed off the river there was that smell of the Sangamon bottomlands, a dampish, fetid odor. It was a smell of wet mud left from many another flood, mud patterned every night with raccoon tracks; it was a smell of old brown leaves left on the ground all winter, and of mushrooms growing on rotten logs. The smell wasn't disagreeable, it was just part of the river, and when Abe remembered the Sangamon he always thought of that aroma of the bottomlands in early spring.

Billy Masters was among the first to come down the hill trail in the morning. Billy was sixteen. His shock of rich dark red hair was usually as unruly as Abe's black locks, and the boy showed promise of one day becoming almost as tall as Abe himself. Billy was full of the excitement of boat building and he yearned desperately to be allowed to go along. Abe said Billy could go if Denton Offutt had no objections, nor Billy's maw and paw. But he didn't know, Mr. Offutt was a peculiar man. Billy was on hand first thing in the morning anyway. If he arrived before the three had eaten, Abe fried an extra slab of pork, put it between two chunks of cold corn pone, and handed him a mug of steaming coffee. To Billy, that was the finest food in the world because it was served with such an air. Towering six-feet-four in his bare feet, his craggy face lit with affection and his whole lank, brawny body radiating a certain poise and dignity, Abe Lincoln, even handing out a corn-pone sandwich, seemed exciting to Billy.

In spite of how he looked, Abe did that to people. He was tall and gaunt and bony, as if he'd never had enough to eat in his life—as if what he had eaten had all gone to bone and muscle —but he was tremendous across the shoulders and his arms were the sort which developed from hewing rails and clearing forests. His clothes looked all too scant for his size. His trousers, which had been his father's, lacked five inches of reaching the ground, though when he stuffed the ends into the tops of his rawhide boots, that took care of the drafts around his ankles. He wore an old round-about which was much too short for him; it had belonged to one of his cousins. This coat was so short that when Abe bent over to take a piece of pork out of the frying pan on the campfire, he showed a wide expanse of shirt and suspenders. His hat was drab-colored and stained. It had a small crown and a broad brim, and was well worn because it, too, had been Tom Lincoln's. But you forgot how Abe looked when he began to talk.

"I declare, Billy," he'd say, fixing him another piece of pone, "if you don't eat more, you'll run to gristle like I did. Here, dip that pone in the grease; almost as good as butter without the trouble of bothering the cow!"

Soon after Billy Masters arrived on the scene he was followed by Walter Carman, Johnny Roll, and John Seamon, and it wasn't long before most of the men and boys of the village, on one excuse or another, had gathered around the hull of the new boat. The brisk smell of fresh oak lumber grew as the sun finally rose high enough to warm the sappy planks, and there was the dull *thud, thud, thud* of mallets pounding the pegs which Abe had set Billy Masters and Johnny Roll to making. Oak pegs would swell when the boat was in the river and all the joints would fit tighter than ever. Billy made so many pegs that he went on making them in his sleep, and could still smell the oak planks warming in the sun and hear the thudding of the mallets, and the men chuckling at Abe's jokes.

There was a log lying on the ground which became known as Abe's log, although more than likely it was the villagers themselves who lined up along it while Abe worked. Somehow he could work and declaim at the same time and he could do a creditable job of both. It made him feel good to reel off poetry, all he could remember, or to burst out in an off-key rendition of "How Tedious and Tasteless the Hours," or maybe the dismal "John Anderson's Lament," while he beat time with a mallet.

13

Or, when he was feeling especially good and had a big audience, he'd start off on one of the orations of Henry Clay or Daniel Webster, both of whom he greatly admired. Billy Masters doubted if either the great Mr. Webster or the honorable Mr. Clay ever could have declaimed one of his own speeches as well as Abe did.

Foot on the log, wind in his hair, big hands waving the mallet for emphasis, he'd go on for twenty minutes from memory. Billy would never forget that day when Abe Lincoln declaimed from Webster—" 'When my eyes shall be turned to behold, for the last time, the sun in heaven, may I not see him shining on the broken and dishonored fragments of a once-glorious Union; on States dissevered, discordant, belligerent; on a land rent with civil feuds, or drenched, it may be, in fraternal blood!' " As Abe lifted his eyes to the sky and flung out his big, eloquent hands, Billy felt shivers of pure delight run up and down his spine. He hung on every word.

" 'Let their last feeble and lingering glance rather behold the glorious ensign of the republic, now known and honored throughout the earth, still full high advanced, its arms and trophies streaming in their original lustre . . . spread all over in characters of living light, blazing on all its ample folds as they float over the sea and over the land.' " Abe waved his hands in a floating motion, and Billy could see the Stars and Stripes waving over America, out, out—" 'And in every wind and under the whole heavens, that sentiment, dear to every American heart—' " And as Abe's voice suddenly dropped in a dramatic hush, everyone leaned forward. Then he roared out—" *'Liberty and Union,* now and forever, One and Inseparable!' "

Billy Masters rolled off the log and clapped till his palms were sore, and the men clapped and stamped and roared, as they did at a political rally for Andy Jackson. Abe bowed low to the cheers. John Hanks and Jack Johnston glowed with pride at Abe's accomplishments. They never had much to say and none of it sparkled, but they could take pride in a kinsman's skill with words. And somehow, with all the horseplay, orating, singing, conversation and haranguing for hours over President Jackson and Henry Clay and Nick Biddle and the United States Bank, the boat was on its way to being finished.

CHAPTER THREE

As ABE AND his assistants worked, spring had come. Abe shed his heavy cowhide boots and threw his hat, his too-short coat, and his vest over a tree branch. In his bare feet and with his shirt wet with perspiration in the suddenly warm days of April, and with his dark hair standing straight on end, he worked from morning until night. Abe knew something about flatboats. Three years before, when he had gone with Allen Gentry from Gentry's Landing in Indiana, down the Ohio and the Mississippi to New Orleans, he had learned what a New Orleans-bound flatboat was supposed to be. This wasn't a little Kentucky boat, content with the Cumberland and the Ohio. This had to be big and strong and well-made and true; otherwise it might lie in ruins on some sand bar down the Mississippi, or even closer to home than that. A constant reminder of a poorly built flatboat lay wrecked across the river from the sawmill. That was the first flatboat ever built along the Sangamon and it hadn't even reached its first destination. The treacherous snags had ruined it.

Abe's flatboat was simple enough—nothing fancy about a flatboat—but he took a peculiar and deep pride in what he was doing. The long, squared timbers were made into a rectangular ark, eighty feet long and eighteen feet wide, with walls seven feet high, then roofed with heavy planks to enclose the cargo. This cabin also was the crew's living quarters. In a sandbox a cooking fire could be built. The crew would sleep in the cabin, but pleasant days would be spent in lounging on the flat roof. The big boat would be steered by a great sweep or steering oar whose construction Abe took care of himself.

He would entrust this vital piece of carpentry to no one else. A defective oar could wreck the boat, for there was no other way to guide or direct the massive freighter on its ponderous passage down three rivers south. Since Abe was the pilot, fully responsible for getting the boat and its cargo safely to its destination, he was going to see to it that the steering oar was strong and true. So he cut down a tall young hickory with an uncommonly straight, slim, long trunk, and he trimmed it and shaped it and put on a paddle blade, and there she was, as good a steering oar as the Mississippi ever would see.

Abe was growing more and more proud of his ship. This was no flimsy raft, no rude flatboat which would go a little way and then would be sold with the produce at the nearest market. This had to hold together for more than a thousand miles down the galloping spring waters of three rivers of middle America. It never would come back to the Illinois country—flatboats were one-way travel—but it had to arrive safely in New Orleans with Denton Offutt's cargo. Denton Offutt may not have been especially particular about the kind of boat he had—he was a carefree soul—but Abraham Lincoln knew what it had to be, and he made it so.

CHAPTER FOUR

WHILE WIRY little Johnny Roll and handsome young Billy Masters turned out oak pegs by the hundreds, Abe put Jack Johnston and Walter Carman to work on a cottonwood canoe to be taken along on the flatboat. Besides, it would keep Jack's mind off his new-found cronies in the village who had shown him how he could make a little easy money by betting on cockfights.

"If one of us wants to go ashore from the flatboat," Abe explained, "we'll need a canoe. Dig it as thin as you can, boys, so it won't weigh any more than it has to."

So Walter and Jack worked on the canoe, and finally the big craft was finished. Thinly as they had tried to work it, this was still a heavy canoe.

"Let's try it out," suggested Jack in a low voice.

"Better let Abe do that, it's his," warned Walter, glancing around. The others were all busy at their jobs.

"Shucks, we made it, we ought to try it and see if it'll float, before we give it to him. Come on." So they took the heavy canoe to the river's edge and shoved it in.

Too late, Abe looked up and saw what they were doing.

"Hey," he cried, "get the other paddle!" But Jack and Walter had leaped into the canoe as soon as it touched the water. As if alive, the craft plunged into the current.

Walter, in the stern, frantically worked the single paddle they had remembered to bring along, but in the surging, boiling, whirling current of the flooding Sangamon, the canoe was at the mercy of the tossing brown water and galloping driftwood which came surging downstream.

Walter desperately wished they were back on land. Jack wished he had had the sense to bring the other paddle. Walter did his best to turn the canoe toward shore, but the current repeatedly swung them until they were in danger of swamping. Then they tried to steer toward the half-submerged wreck, one of whose stanchions still was standing above the water. As the canoe bounded past the stanchion, Jack reached out wildly and grasped it so firmly that he was lifted neatly out of the craft. At the jolt, Walter was thrown into the water. The cottonwood canoe went leaping over the rapids and was on its independent way without them.

As if they were watching a play, everybody on shore stood transfixed. It had all happened so suddenly and with such speed that even if the onlookers could have thought of a means of rescue, there was no time for anyone to do anything. Now the men came alive. They shouted. They yelled advice. They roared directions. They waved their arms and ran up and down but accomplished nothing toward getting the two out of the river. Jack was still gripping the stanchion and Walter was doing his best to swim in the eddying river.

"Head for that big tree!" shouted Abe, and pointed to a great elm which normally grew on shore but which now, in high water, was surrounded by the boiling current. "Head for the tree and hang on!" Walter, panicky with fear and feebly struggling with the current, cried out, "I can't make it!" He promptly swallowed a mouthful of muddy water.

"You've got to, it's your only chance!" yelled Abe. Somehow you always did what Abe said, and so Walter dog-paddled and wallowed and finally got to the elm. He held on to a low horizontal branch.

"Pull yourself up—you'll be swept away!" directed Abe. And Walter dragged himself heavily out of the water and perched weakly on a big limb. Like a wet and miserable crow, Walter Carman, surrounded by the angry Sangamon that licked at the tree in which he sat, shivered in the April wind and wondered how he would ever get to shore.

But Jack Johnston's plight was worse, and Abe himself began to feel a panic of fear grip his heart as he saw how far down into the water the boy had slipped. If he let go his grip, he would be swept away in the current, and few men could live very long in the spring eddies of the Sangamon. If anything happened to Jack—Abe thought of his stepmother, Sarah Lincoln, who loved him as much as she loved her own boy, and how he, Abe, had promised her when they started off from the cabin that he would see that Jack returned home safely.

"I know he'll be safe with you, Abe," his stepmother had said, pressing his hands in her own work-hardened ones. "You know how Jack is, ready to do any wild thing that comes along. Watch out for him, boy. Don't let him do anything reckless, I pray you, Abe. And take care of yourself." Then she had kissed them both good-bye. If anything happened to Jack—to either of them, for that matter—Sarah Lincoln would be plunged into deep sorrow for her lost boys.

"Jack!" Abe yelled with determination in his voice. "You swim to that tree! Hear me? *Swim to that tree!*"

Jack shook his head stiffly and stared at the churning flood.

"Swim!" ordered Abe desperately. The boy just had to swim.

Jack shook his head again. Then in anguished fear he let go of the stanchion and slid into the river. He was churned up and down like a cork until he struck out through the cold water.

Jack splashed and kicked—and he swam. He went under once and Billy Masters thought he was a goner. Abe gripped his big hands and wrung them in agony because there was nothing he could do to help the boy. But Jack came up again. A floating log coming downstream headed maliciously straight toward him. He did not see the approaching danger until he heard Abe yell.

"Watch it, boy!" cried Abe, as he saw the log coming toward the swimmer's head. Even if he had had the strength left to do so, Jack saw it too late to get out of the way. And he went down again.

Billy thought his own heart had stopped beating. Abe groaned. And then the men cheered, and there was Jack Johnston again. He had ducked and the log had gone over him. At last, his strength ebbing fast, the boy reached the elm and pulled himself on to the branch with Walter. Abe gave a deep, involuntary sigh and let his hands drop to his sides.

There were two wet and shivering birds in the tree, and still they were not much closer to rescue than they had been before. The canoe had long since disappeared. There was no other boat at hand.

Women with their shawls wrapped around their heads and their aprons around their arms came running down the hill, and their cries and gabbling made such a racket Abe could hardly think. All the men and boys of the town were there, and everyone had a different solution to the problem. Meanwhile, the two in the tree were growing colder and weaker. Unless they were rescued soon they would drop off into the water.

Abe took charge. Nobody else did. It seemed to be his job. Seldom in his lifetime had there been a chance to take charge of anything or to organize anything. His father had always been the one to make decisions in that family.

"You keep yore mouth shet, Abe," he'd say sternly when Abe offered an idea, perhaps to repair a broken axle or a way to put stronger hinges on the door. "This is man's work and you ain't a man yet!"

Maybe Abe was too big to be thrashed, but his paw knew how to lay a whip into his spirit and kill his dreams and plans. But now along the Sangamon Abe was boss.

"Get that log over there, boys," he said, pointing toward the well-polished log which had been used for weeks as a seat for Abe's admirers, "and a good strong rope." He fastened the rope around the log—so—and while Billy and Jim Dorrell galloped along beside him to help, Abe towed the log upstream.

"Hop on, Jim," invited Abe, "and ride that log down to the tree. I'll control it with the rope, and when you get near the tree, sling a loop over a limb to cut your speed, then pull it up to the tree trunk so those two can get on it."

Jim Dorrell was one of the wild young fellows of the village. He was the sort to ride a crazy-mad steer or head the gang of toughs at goose-pullings. He was chief organizer of cock fights and wrestling bouts. Riding a wild log was just his dish. He leaped on and flung his legs around the log, waved his hat and whooped and hollered while the log bounded with the pushing brown water. Abe, running on the shore, held the rope firmly so that the log wouldn't go out into the main current. But when it approached the tree, just as Abe had planned for it to do, Jim Dorrell lost his head and grabbed a branch instead of cinching the rope around it. And so the log was neatly snaked out from under him, and there was Jim dangling with his legs in the water. Sheepishly, he pulled himself up on the branch, and then there were three wet and shivering fellows sitting in that elm. For a quick instant Abe thought that if it wasn't so blamed serious, it would be downright funny. But at this moment it was not a laughing matter. Time enough to laugh later when he had fulfilled his promise to his mother and got Jack safely on land again.

Abe pulled the log back to shore and tightened the rope around it. Again he towed it upstream and allowed it to float down with the current, but this time Abe himself rolled up his pants, got astride and, as he would have gripped a bucking horse, he gripped the log with his bony knees. Guided by Caleb Carman and Aaron Saunders, the log, as if it knew a master's touch, obediently drifted toward the tree.

Abe threw a rope over the stub of a branch to break the speed of the log, and then, slowly, slowly, drew it up under the limb where the three were perched in abject, dripping misery.

He held the log steady. "Climb on, boys," he directed. "Careful now, Walter, don't you upset us—hey, watch out, we almost capsized that time! Jack next. Careful—get on easy. Now Jim—that was a fool thing you did, boy. All right, leave room for me." He cast off the rope loop and, "Pull us in!" he shouted.

Caleb Carman and Aaron Saunders, with willing assistance from everyone who could catch hold of the rope, eased the log through the current and brought its riders safely to shore.

"Three cheers for Abe Lincoln!" shouted William Broadwell, throwing his hat into the air. And "Three cheers for Abe!" they all yelled. Abe was the last to climb off the log.

Abe Lincoln was a hero, the hero of the Sangamon!

CHAPTER FIVE

Spring moved into the Sangamon Country. Abe Lincoln heard geese flying over on the misty nights, had seen a great flock of curlews out on the short-grass prairie. And one morning when the wind was from the south and the perfume of the wild plums scented the air with a fragrance that made him both sad and happy, there came a distant roaring. It sounded like a high wind, far off.

"Listen, hear that!" spoke up John, dropping his mallet. "Sounds like a tornado to me. Big wind."

"Wrong kind of weather, John," commented Abe, looking with puzzled eyes at the clear sky. With such a sky and in such a fresh, cool breeze, a tornado would be unlikely. "But it surely does sound like wind, for a fact."

It came nearer, nearer. The roaring filled the air. Then suddenly the sun was dimmed as a moving black cloud spread across the south and climbed over the sky. From up in the direction of the village the boat crew could hear a sudden strange banging and clattering, a racket as of a hundred pots and pans rattling behind a peddler's cart.

And then the dark cloud swerved and, with a rush of wings that shook the trees, a horde of wild pigeons veered and came down—passenger pigeons migrating north. The forest was full of them, full of their talking and murmuring; the trees rustled with the force of wind from millions of wings, bent under the weight of slim, iridescent bodies. Branches on the maples cracked off and fell. Up on the hill at the village there still were sounds of banging and screaming.

"There's trouble up there!" cried Abe. He and the others dropped their tools and, dodging falling limbs and flapping pigeons, raced up the hill. There were pigeons everywhere, everywhere, birds too unafraid to move out of the path until they were brushed aside where they lay fluttering their opalescent wings.

Abe and the others reached the village to find all the womenfolk and children beating on pans, waving aprons and making a clatter to scare the birds out of the gardens. Peas, corn, and early lettuce were just up and the pigeons, down by thousands in the fields, were eating every spear of green they could find. Noise and motion did not bother them. They only moved and came down in another place.

Mrs. Carman was in tears. "All my nice peas gone!"

Mrs. Babcock was running about like a madwoman, flapping her apron and screaming at the birds. "*Shoo*—get away, you filthy things—*shoo!*"

On the tavern porch sat old Ahab Littleford, wrapped in shawls and sunning himself. He cackled and chuckled at all the commotion and at how the women were flapping about.

"Like a passel of fool geese, not gettin' nowhere!"

The children were excitedly running around with sticks, hitting pigeons left and right. The birds were easily struck and killed. The men came with guns and blasted into the flocks, and dead or dying birds came fluttering down like heavy fruits. The children and dogs ran to pick them up. Yet the great murmuring and rustling and the cracking of tree branches under the weight of millions of birds went on as if they were undisturbed by the death of a few.

Suddenly—as suddenly as it had come, and as if at a signal—there was another tremendous roaring. Passenger pigeons got up out of the trees and out of the denuded gardens and out of the woods; the sky again was darkened with them as they flew north across the Sangamon, across the flooded lowlands, north toward their nesting grounds.

Grimly, the villagers looked at their gardens. The women wiped their tears and the children gathered up all the pigeons they could carry and left the rest to the dogs and cats and hogs, and to the possums which would come in the night to clean up what was left. Almost every home in Sangamo Town served wild pigeon for supper that day—pigeon pot pie, pigeon with dumplings, pigeon stew, roast pigeon. But the young peas and the young lettuce, and the delicate feathers of corn, all had been nipped off so close to the ground that you could hardly know where they had been. Because the gardens would have to be re-planted, and the people knew it, they took grim satisfaction out of eating their pigeon dinners that evening.

Abe and the others went back to the bottoms to drag away the fallen branches from their work space.

As in all wildernesses, the comings and goings of the wild creatures had their influence upon the people who were settling there. Not only the villagers, but Abe and his kinsmen as well, surrounded by the creatures of the Illinois springtime, sometimes were mightily disturbed by them.

One night in the bottoms, the barred owls shouted and yapped and purred at their courting in the old trees, until Jack

Johnston, shuddering, said it made his blood run cold to hear them.

"I don't like it," he complained. "It's dangerous, that's what it is, to live down here with them awful sounds. I don't believe they're just birds; they're lost and tormented sperrits, that's what they are!" Jack paused in the light of the campfire where he was mending a rip in his trousers. Living in the shanty and working in the river forest plagued him incessantly with torn clothing and dirt he could never avoid.

But when, that evening, there came a quavering wailing from right on top of them, so it seemed, and they discovered a red screech owl on the shanty roof—an owl looking with glistening yellow eyes down at them—John Hanks was scared. He picked up a stone and heaved it at the owl, and it opened its curving ruddy wings and made a sudden swooping dive straight at John Hanks's head. The bird knocked off his hat before swerving up again into the darkness of the rooftop.

"Oh, my soul!" John Hanks cried with alarm which Abe never had seen in him before. His face was pale and his eyes were wide. "Screech owls perchin' on a roof are the worst kind of bad luck, and a red owl means death, sure enough, or bad trouble, anyway. Oh, my soul!" John mourned. "I wisht I hadn't left home. Maybe somethin' is goin' to happen to my wife . . . maybe I'll never live to get home again, and then who'll take keer of my children? I knew I shouldn't have listened to you, Abe Lincoln! A red screech owl!" Somewhere off in the soft night an owl still wailed.

John Hanks took a handful of salt from the little wooden box in which it was kept and flung the grains into the fire.

"That'll help," he said hopefully. He laid the twig-broom across the doorsill of the shanty. "Too bad we ain't got a poker.

If I heated it red-hot and walked around the house with it, he'd go away and the spell'd be broken. But maybe the salt and the broom will do it." An owl wailed again. John threw more salt on the fire, which blazed up yellow.

"Don't use up all our salt, John," said Abe quietly. "We haven't got much left." But John was listening. Off in the distance an owl called thinly, and then they heard it no more.

"You got to watch out for bad-luck birds," said Jack sagely. "I heard a whip-o-will callin' a couple nights past and they was a bird peckin' at the window pane up at William Miller's house three days ago, and you see what happened—old Callie Miller up and died yesterday. It don't pay to fool around when you hear a bad-luck bird; you got to know how to charm away the bad luck."

"What's there to do about a whip-o-will?" asked Abe curiously. "You hear 'em all around, these nights."

"Oh, you just point your finger at the bird and pretty soon it'll stop its cryin' and fly away. Trouble is to see it; it allus cries in the darkness."

"Oh, they's lots of things you got to watch around birds," added John Hanks, feeling more assured. "If you kill a robin, the cows'll give bloody milk. I seen it happen back in Indiana, and if you kill the swallows, you sure will have a run of bad luck all through the year. Don't pay to fool around with 'em."

Abe threw more sticks on the fire so that it blazed brightly. The owl did not call again. "Well, I guess there isn't much you can do about it when you're down in the woods like this," he remarked. "The birds got here first and there're too many of 'em to be pointing your finger at every whip-o-will or wasting a handful of good salt on every owl." He looked reprovingly at John Hanks. "I reckon I'll take my chances."

CHAPTER SIX

Daily now, with mounting alarm, Abe Lincoln watched the river level dropping. If it receded too far—if the flood crest passed and the Sangamon, with its usual speed in any change, lost the fast current which could carry a heavy boat to meet the Illinois—then they were stranded. The venture would have failed—Denton Offutt would lose his produce, John, Jack, and Abe would lose their pay; and they would not get to New Orleans. Maybe never again in their lives would they have a chance like this. Abe pushed the work on the great flatboat, but even with assistance and with longer hours, it still would not be finished for another week.

Abe had figured that they would be ready to go on April eighteenth. Denton Offutt, who had been around to see how the boat was progressing, was coming with his hogs and barrels of produce on the seventeenth. But the river level was falling visibly. Abe lost his appetite. His cooking grew worse. He talked little. There was a deep, dark, morose look in his eyes and there were no jokes told to lighten the hours of work. Day after day the sun shone hotly and day after day the Sangamon went lower. The elm where the three assistants had been stranded a few weeks earlier stood on dry land on the bank. The boat itself lay too far away from the water to be shoved in. Abe had figured that if he built it at a certain distance from the high water, there would be no trouble with the launching. Why, they'd need six teams of oxen to haul that big Mississippi flatboat out to the river channel.

Five days before the scheduled launching, which Abe with melancholy foreboding was sure would never take place, the hot south wind blew hard all morning, but by late afternoon the sky had grown darker and darker; a blue-black mass of clouds rose rapidly out of the west. The wind swirled through the trees; new leaves like tattered feathers flew on the gusts. Abe, in some anxiety, sent Billy Masters home before the storm broke. Work on the boat halted and tools were hastily put into the shanty—just in time. The rain came with a rush and the forest was instantly enveloped in a gray blur. The river bottoms were deserted. Men of the village, with heads bent against the gale, hurried to shelter on the hill. Abe and his kinsmen dashed into the makeshift shanty which shook under the force of the wind. And the storm was a living presence that raged through the forests of the Sangamon, breaking off branches and roaring lustily.

After a while the wind lessened and the thunder and lightning moved off into the east, but the rain continued in a steady downpour. When morning came grayly into the bottoms, it was still pouring. Even the frogs had hushed their yelping and not a bird sang. There was no use in trying to work on the boat, but in spite of this delay, Abe felt only delight as he looked out, from time to time, and noticed that the river was rising. Maybe—if only this rain continued long enough—the flatboat still would have a chance to travel the river's meandering course. Perhaps he would get back to New Orleans after all.

Inside the shanty there was nothing to do but wait. Abe

couldn't make a fire because he and his companions had not bothered to build an indoor fireplace; and since the outdoors was as wet as the forty days and forty nights, the menu featured cold food. The rain began seeping under the plank walls; the dirt floor was getting puddly; the shanty was rapidly growing unlivable. Abe, Jack, and John piled their pallets and blankets on the plank table and went up the muddy hill to Caleb Carman's tavern.

In Sangamo Town, rain was pounding in the streets, and mud and water stood knee-deep. There wasn't a person about; no horses were hitched to the rails; even the carding mill was silent. On such a day, nobody had tried to bring in bags of wool to be carded. Abe and his kinsmen sloshed up on the tavern porch, where they stamped the wet and mud off themselves, as others before them evidently had done. The wet chickens, gathered there with dismally sagging tails, pecked half-heartedly at the clods. Mud-time in Illinois was a fearful thing for man, beast and fowl to live through. It was something they had to endure between winter and summer.

Walter heard Abe, John, and Jack on the porch and threw open the door.

"Come in, fellers, come in!" he cried. "No work on the boat today, I'll lay to that!"

They hung their wet coats to dry and gathered around the warm fire. Ben Easley was there, and William Miller, and old Ahab Littleford, Walter's feeble grandfather, who sat huddled in blankets in a big chair nearest the fire. All but Abe and the old man got up a game of Seven-Up at a deal table in the middle of the big room. Mrs. Carman, in her trim blue calico, moved about the fireplace, sweeping up the ashes, brushing off the mantel. She worked deftly and quietly. It was somehow com-

fortable to be in a big house like this, with a warm fire and a
woman moving about to make things neat.

Pretty soon Billy Masters, who had seen the bedraggled trio
arrive, came sprinting down the muddy street, hurdling the
puddles, and entered the tavern. Billy looked glum.

"Matter, Billy?" questioned Abe, his keen eyes on the boy's
unhappy, freckled face. "Bite a wormy apple?"

"Naw, worse than that," said Billy morosely. "Maw and Paw
won't let me go with you on the boat. Said I'm too young, 'n'
they need me. But I'll show 'em. I'll run away and go along with
you anyhow!"

"Now, Billy," soothed Abe, awkwardly laying his hand on the
boy's shoulder. "You do what your mother and father say and
you'll come out all right. I wouldn't go to running away—you'll
never get anywhere doing that, not really. You'll have plenty
of time to go places; this isn't your last chance."

"Maybe it is," groaned Billy, in the depths of despair. "I'm
sixteen. Maybe I'll be stuck here always in this blamed mud and
never know any other kind of life but leaky shacks and corn-
pone and farmin' stumpland. I want to see somethin' of the
world, Abe—I want to git away and better myself. Jes' 'cause my
folks are satisfied is no reason I have to be, is it, Abe?"

"No, Billy, it isn't," Abe answered soberly, remembering the
primitive cabin where he was born, and the cabin, which was
not much better in spite of Sarah Lincoln's best efforts, where
they had all lived last winter. "No, Billy, you got to better
yourself, but maybe this just isn't the time to start. Your time'll
come if you see to it right.

"There's a whole lot more to the world than log cabins and
corn pone," he went on. "Why, in New Orleans, you'll never
believe me, there are fine big houses three stories high with

32

galleries—that's what they call their porches—all fenced with iron twisted into the prettiest shapes—birds, leaves, flowers. You'd never believe it till you saw it. And the way folk dress, like a party all the time!" In the ardor of remembering, Abe failed to notice the determined gleam which had come into Billy's eyes as he listened to the wonders of New Orleans. "No, Billy," Abe went on reflectively, "there's more to living than the way it is here on the prairie. I guess the Lord made the prairie and the mud for a purpose, but there are times when I can't figure out what it is!"

Billy's keen blue eyes didn't meet Abe's gray ones. Billy knew what he wanted to do, and a wild plan was forming in his head.

He and Abe turned to the others around the fire. From wet coats and soaked rawhide boots there rose into the warm room a rank odor which grew thicker as the hours passed.

Ahab Littleford directed his gaze sharply at each man and then came to rest on Abe. He beckoned impatiently with his claw-like hand.

"Howdy, Mr. Littleford," said Abe agreeably, coming over to sit close to the chair so that the deaf ears could catch what he said. "It's a mighty poorly sort of day. We got rained out of the bottoms and nigh got drowned out of our shanty. Inch of water on the floor—if you want to call it a floor. I'd just as soon call it a frog-pond. For a fact, I found a frog sitting on my bed cover this morning, staring me in the face bold as brass!"

"You boys better sleep up here till the water goes down," quavered the old man, but his eyes twinkled as he thought of the frog. "How's the boat comin', boy?" he went on eagerly. "Abe, boy, mind you finish that flatboat good and don't you let nothin' happen to it. This is your chanct to take part of the Sangamon Country down to Newerleans and make somethin' o' yourself

33

at the same time."

"Well, don't know as I'll do much of that last," said Abe doubtfully, winking at Billy. "I'm only a riverman and likely always will be."

"No, you ain't, Abe Lincoln! No, you ain't!" cried Ahab Littleford excitedly, pounding with his cane on the floor.

"Now, Paw, don't you get all het up," warned Mrs. Carman with a look at Abe. "Don't let him git riled, will you, Abe? It ain't good fer him."

"I'll git riled all I want, girl. You shet your mouth and leave me be. Guess I know what I want to say and it's a fine thing if a man of my years cain't say what he wants. Now you listen, Abe Lincoln. I knew your grandpap down in Kaintucky. Come up the Wilderness Road with him and his family. His name were Abraham Lincoln, too, same as you, and there never was a braver man. What a time we had agoin' up over all them jagged rocks of that there Cumberland Gap! I swear it was the hardest trail *I* ever see, but they said it was the easiest way over into Kaintucky. Old Abe, he stopped somewhere, I disremember where, but I built me a cabin up near Boonesboro. And I heerd later he got kilt by Injuns. He was a brave man, your grandpap, boy, and you kin be like him."

"I sure do appreciate hearing about him," said Abe soberly.

"Well, I got farther away nor he did," cackled old Ahab Littleford with satisfaction. "*I* got me to Sangamo Town and *I* didn't git kilt by no Injuns, but I ain't goin' no farther, I know that, not till the Trump o' Doom calls, 'Ahab Littleford, air you thar?' And I'll jist riz my box lid right up and knock over my tombstone, and I'll come right up out of that Sangamon County gumbo and answer, 'Yes, Lord, I'm here, and I *been* ready a blame long time!' "

34

"Oh, now, Mr. Littleford, you'll be with us years yet," soothed Abe as the old man ceased his rambling, waved his stick, and rolled his eyes.

"Careful, Paw," said Mrs. Carman, in back of his chair.

"Careful, nothin', girl," roared Ahab. "Clear out and leave us men alone. Always a woman got to meddle in with her twittle-twattle and her warnin'—'be keerful, Paw—don't exert yourself, Paw—you mought tire yourself, Paw,'" he shrilled. "Bah! Leave me alone, I say.

"Abe," he went on in a different tone, "don't you stay in this here backwoods. Git out and make suthin' of yourself. Your grandpap would if he'd a lived."

Abe laughed. "Sounds like you and Billy here been getting your ideas out of the same bucket! Billy's been pestering me to go along on the boat, wants to make something of *him*self, too, only his mother won't let him go."

"Mind your maw, son," said the old man, frowning at young Billy Masters. "When you git old enough to shave's plenty time enough to git out of here. Meanwhile, you be good to your maw, boy. She's a mighty fine woman, mighty fine."

Talk moved into other channels. The smell of baking corn pone in a spider on the hearth mingled with the smells of the tavern. Outside, the gray rain slanted into the mud and made deeper puddles, and a soaked rooster drooped unhappily under the porch.

Abe and his kinsmen stayed at Caleb Carman's tavern until the rain let up. It poured for three days and work on the boat was at a standstill. But the river was rising. Even from the hilltop they could hear its louder roaring as the boiling current carried sycamores that had crumpled off the caving banks and came bounding and plunging along, or caught in the branches of trees standing in the flood. The river was rising! It was coming higher into the bottoms. And Abe was sure that his boat would float, would ride strongly and surely down the Sangamon to meet the more reliable depths of the Illinois.

When Abe went down to see how matters stood, he found the floor of the shack two inches under water. The place where the flatboat stood on its chocks was covered with a foot of water which was rising higher by the hour.

Abe's heart gave a flip-flop of fear. There were only a few inches more to go before the water would lap the hull of the big flatboat. Another foot and the craft would be awash, could float away and be ruined in the snags and trees, could even get out on the open river and be lost. Although the other worry about low water was vanquished with the coming of the rains, Abe found a new worry in this menace of the rapidly rising flood which threatened to undo all his work and ruin all his plans.

He splashed back up the hill and borrowed all the heavy rope he could find. Then Abe, John, and Jack hustled down and tethered the flatboat from all points to the strong white sycamores and maples.

"Now let her get away!" said Abe, but he slept uneasily that night. If only they could get the boat finished and be on their way!

The rain finally stopped. The high water in the bottoms seeped back into the river, and although the lowlands were covered with slimy mud and debris, the river still ran high. It was high enough to carry a heavy flatboat on its way.

THE BOYS YELLED AND THE DOGS BARKED AND THE HOGS SQUEALED AND
TRUMPETED AS THEY CHARGED DESPERATELY . . . UP THE PLANK

ABE TRIED TO STOP THE BIG BOAT BEFORE SHE WAS WRECKED. SHE STOPPED
ALL RIGHT, STOPPED WITH A SICKENING CRUNCH

CHAPTER SEVEN

THE FLATBOAT was finished. The last peg had been hammered firmly into its hole. The last board had been fastened snugly against its neighbor. The sandbox was in the cabin, ready for its first cook fire on the voyage. Abe stood back and viewed his masterpiece.

"She needs something," he mused, hand on chin. "I know what it is, Billy," he added suddenly. "She needs a mast and sail. It would give her more speed—we're going to need it, too—and it would give her an air besides."

He hunted around in the discarded lumber and found a tall, strong hickory pole which would do for a crude mast.

"Now, what can we find for a sail?"

Billy had an idea at once. "My maw will let you have a piece of canvas, I know she will. We got some left from what we used to cover the Conestoga wagon when we come out here from Pennsylvania." And Billy was off up the hill. He pelted back with a rather dirty and patched piece of canvas which Abe somehow tailored into a rude sail. A little breeze drifted along and the canvas bellied out properly, and Abe and Billy both felt that it indeed completed the boat and gave her quite a fine and jaunty air. At last the flatboat was really finished.

That evening Abe went up on the hill to bid good-bye to old Ahab Littleford, who looked more shrunken than ever. Abe also said good-bye to Mrs. Carman and to old Mrs. Abbott, who would be unable to get up and out to see the launching. Somehow he was sorry to leave all these kind people on the Sangamo Town hill.

Next he paid a call on Mrs. Masters. Billy was not in sight. He had been visibly moping all day.

"Well, Abe, I'm glad to see you," cried Mrs. Masters cordially, shaking his big hard hand. "Billy has been near driving me crazy wanting to go with you tomorrow."

"I know, ma'am," Abe replied, watching her face as it lost its bright look and lines and hollows appeared. "I'd like mighty well to take him, too. We get along together, Mrs. Masters. Billy's a fine boy and he's been a big help to me. He'd earn his keep on the boat and I'd owe him money besides."

"Abe, I wish I could let him go!" the woman cried. "But I just can't. I need him here. I haven't told him, and I won't till it's needful, but his daddy ain't well. He's been having bad spells, and Doctor Allen over to New Salem says it's his heart. I'm afeared he'll keel over dead any day. And I can't let Billy go. You see how it is, don't you, Abe? It ain't like I want to make the boy unhappy keeping him home. He's got to be here in case something happens to his daddy."

Abe laid a gentle hand on Mrs. Masters' shaking one.

"Don't you be afraid, ma'am. Billy'll stay. I'll see to that!"

CHAPTER EIGHT

It was April eighteenth. On that fine, shining, singing spring morning most of the people of Sangamo Town trooped down the wagon road to the shore. The Sheppards left the grist mill, Johnny Roll's parents and Billy Masters' family, and the Abbotts and the Broadwells and the Sweringens and the Lacys all came— men, women, and children. Caleb Carman locked the tavern and Ben McElwain closed up the carding mill. Between them they made a chair of their hands and carried Ahab Littleford down to the shore. The old man was determined not to miss the launching.

Everyone gathered on the river bank to watch the greatest event that ever had happened in Sangamo Town. There it lay, Abraham Lincoln's flatboat, big and broad and dependable, floating now in the muddy Sangamon. No danger of that boat foundering, everyone said admiringly, examining how the planks were pegged together, how compactly the roofed-over deck was built.

Now all the men pitched in and helped load the flatboat. Denton Offutt had come with a drove of hogs, and other men had come with wagons loaded with his barrels of pork and corn meal and flour. The men rounded up the cantankerous hogs that were scattered in the bottoms, and put the younger boys to chasing porkers that had run too far afield. The boys joyfully set the dogs on them, and there was a mighty hullabaloo down in the river bottoms. The boys yelled and the dogs barked, and the hogs squealed and trumpeted as they charged desperately, with a dog hanging on each ear, up the plank to the pen on deck. Old Ahab Littleford sat in a wagon bed and cackled and laughed and waved his stick.

The whole business was generaled by Denton Offutt himself, decked in his best clothes. Now that the boat was finished, he appeared in time to order everyone around in a grand show of self-importance.

At last the flatboat was loaded. More cargo would be put on at Beardstown, where the hogs would be taken off. Abe thanked his stars for that. A load of hogs wouldn't do anything to help the beauty of his new boat.

And then they were ready to cast off. At that moment some of the young fellows of the village, including Walter Carman and John Seamon and Johnny Roll and Jim Dorrell, climbed aboard, too, and perched on the cabin for a ride. Old Ahab Littleford, with tears of vexation in his eyes, wished desperately that he was young and spry enough to be perching there on the roof of that big boat. He slapped angrily at the mosquitoes and with an intent glare watched everything that was happening. Everyone else slapped mosquitoes, too, but not one would miss this launching for any amount of insects.

Nobody had seen Billy Masters all morning.

"Hey, Mr. Littleford," Abe, on the deck of the flatboat, called out over the crowd. "You seen Billy Masters? We're about to cast off and he'll want to see us go."

Ahab shook his head fiercely. "Little pup," he muttered, "don't have the sense to know what he's missin'!"

The crew shook hands all around and then climbed aboard again. Abe, tall and lank in his too-short pants and coat, stood at the long steering oar. Denton Offutt was trying to deliver a speech but couldn't make himself heard. John Hanks looked morose, and Jack Johnston, well brushed and with his boots polished, was making an impression on the girls. And the crowd on deck laughed and joked and waved.

The ropes were untied. The flatboat, like a frightened steer, leaped into the racing current. The hogs tumbled against each other and squealed and snorted, the barrels adjusted themselves, and Denton Offutt lost his balance and sat down hard, amid the laughter of the passengers and crew and cheering on shore. The boat was on its way. Ahab Littleford, with tears now running down his sunken cheeks, stood up in the wagon bed and waved his cane as long as the boat was in sight.

But Abe lost some of the triumph of the launching because young Billy Masters was not there to see it. Billy must be angry with him for not letting him go. Abe, with his mouth set in a firm, tight line, manned the long steering oar as the boat swept down the river.

With a grand surge of freedom, the craft was on its way down the straight channel between the tall maples of the bottoms. The big hill stood on the left and the swampy plain lay to the right. Flocks of black coots got up out of Pearson Roll's flooded corn-field and flew low over the water as the boat moved swiftly down the channel and around the first bend.

New leaves like pale red and amber lace sparkled on the maples. Young green leaves were on the elms. Papaws were in bloom, and spicebush made a golden haze of blossoms in the April air. The rude sail of the flatboat caught the breeze and sent it along at four to five miles an hour. In deep satisfaction that warmed the inside of him, Abe thought, this speed is wonderful!

At Lemon's Bend, two and one-half miles downstream from Sangamo Town, there was a convenient place to pull in and permit the passengers reluctantly to get off. None of them really wanted to leave; it was such fun riding with Abe. Only John Hanks, perhaps, would have been willing to get off and stay off. John's distaste for the whole trip was mounting. A thousand times he had regretted his decision to come along with Abe and Jack, but Abe never would listen to his arguments for going back home.

"We need you, John," Abe would say firmly. "You promised to make the trip with us and you've got to come. You'll like it once we get on our way. And your family'll do all right till you get back. Paw will help look after them, and Mother will, too. No, John, you've got to come." But that didn't make John any more eager to do it.

After the crowd had left at Lemon's Bend, John went below to the cabin and was about to pick up a blanket which he found on the floor, when the blanket rolled out of the way and John fell back with a yell of surprise.

"Hey, Abe, we got a passenger!" he shouted up the hatch. "Friend of yours, forgot to git off!" Billy Masters sheepishly grinned from the darkness of the cabin up into the sunshine of the deck.

"Well, I declare!" cried Abe in exasperation. "Didn't I say you couldn't go along? Why didn't you get off back there at the Bend when you had a chance? Boy, you ought to be horsewhipped, and I for one hope your daddy gives it to you when you get back!"

"I ain't goin' back," said Billy.

"Yes, you are," said Abe, remembering Mrs. Masters' troubled eyes. "Next stop we make, off you go."

CHAPTER NINE

ABE SAW what was coming before they struck. Instead of three feet of water sliding silkenly over the milldam below New Salem hill, he could see the logs of the dam—the water had dropped! He braced himself for the jolt, but it nearly tore his arms from their sockets as he tried to stop the big boat before she was wrecked. She stopped all right, stopped with a sickening crunch and settled backward with the stern in the water and the bow hanging awkwardly over the dam. Water began pouring into the stern.

Abe let go the steering oar. It hadn't broken—that carefully selected green hickory wouldn't break easily. His arms hadn't broken, either, though they ached like fury. He felt terrible inside, desperately, horribly sick and mortified at how he'd wrecked their beautiful boat—*his* boat, for all that Denton Offutt had paid for it.

Denton Offutt had fallen among the hogs and was screaming for help to get out. Abe, as if dazed, helped him up, set him on his feet, and brushed him off. Jack Johnston had tumbled backward into the river. Furious at the state his clothes were in, and scared to look at Abe, he scrambled soggily on deck. Billy Masters just looked miserable. He'd wanted excitement but he hadn't bargained for this. Somehow it made him feel as if it were his own fault.

Abe was grim. There was a white line along his jaw and his eyes were like gray stones.

"Where's John?" he asked, just as John Hanks, in great alarm, poked his head up from the cabin. "Hey, what's happened? We're shippin' water and it's comin' into the cabin!"

Abe slid down the hatch to see. Water in the stern was ankle deep and getting deeper. His knees felt weak.

"We've got to get the cargo unloaded," he said in a low voice. "Water's coming in and we've got to lighten her so she will rise and we can drain her out."

"If we could all get out in the river and push, maybe we could get her off," suggested Jack, not too hopefully. The idea of more work in the form of unloading barrels and hogs was full of anguish to him.

"She's too big. Besides, loaded as she is, she'd nose down in the mud and that'd be the end of everything, boat *and* cargo. No, we've got to unload her, at least part of it, then shove the rest forward to lighten the stern," muttered Abe, planning as he talked.

"*I* vote we let Mr. Offutt take keer of it from now on in," snapped John Hanks, who had lost all his patience with the expedition. "I vote we git off and walk home and leave Mr. Offutt to *dis*-pose of his hogs and barr'ls to the highest bidder and leave this here boat where she is. I'm sick of the whole thing, that I am!"

Abe just looked at his cousin, who dropped his eyes. Denton Offutt was scared. He could feel his profits oozing out of his pockets and great holes of indebtedness creeping into them instead.

"You can't do that to me!" he shrilled in deeply injured tones. "Here I hire you, Abe Lincoln, to carry my cargo safely to N'Orleans and what do you do? You wreck it on the first little piddlin' dam you come to. How you goin' to git down the Illinois *and* the Mississippi if you cain't even git it down the Sangamon? I'll be ruined, that's what. Ruined! I w-want a drink!" And tears ran down the plump little man's mottled face.

"I'll see that you get a drink, Mr. Offutt," said Abe in a dangerously quiet voice. "And I'll get your boat off this dam and take her to New Orleans like I said, I vow I will. Now you get in that skiff that's starting out from shore. They're coming out from the mill to help, I see. That's good. You go on up to New Salem at the top of the hill and have refreshment. I'll call you when we get this boat off the dam and ready to go."

The skiff pulled up to the flatboat. Two men were aboard.

"You're ruinin' my dam!" called John Camron. "Cain't you git it off quick 'fore the logs give way?"

Abe shook his head. "Give us time," he said patiently. "We'll get off soon as we can, and gladly. We'll pay for any damage we do," he added, inwardly hoping there was enough money among the crew to pay for damages.

"You sure are in a peck of trouble, ain't you?" remarked Peter Lukins. "How you think to get it off? Kin we help?"

"Don't know yet," said Abe, holding onto his patience. "But I'll be mighty obliged if you'll take Mr. Offutt here over to shore and see that he has a drink while we get ourselves unstuck. Mr. Offutt is considerable upset and needs a little stimulant. Meanwhile, we've got work to do."

The fat little man clambered shakily into the skiff and, talking volubly about his woes all the way, was rowed to shore.

"Cain't trust any man these days," his plaintive voice went

46

on and on in the distance. "Wrecked my boat, he did, ruined my cargo!"

"Now, then, let's start to work," said Abe, his face clearing. "You, John, hail the ferryboat to come over here. We've got to unload this whole blamed boat so her stern will rise and we can drain her."

"Unload *all* of it?" moaned John Hanks. "I tell you, Abe, I wish I'd stayed home. I warned you that red owl was certain sure bad luck. We had nothin' but trouble ever since!"

"Oh, be quiet, John," snapped Abe, his temper wearing thin. "The water's dropped, that's all. No owl rightly could be blamed for that. We'll only unload enough to lighten the weight. I told Mr. Offutt I'd take his boat to New Orleans, and I'm going to do it, if I have to carry it there on my back!"

The ferry came. Boats full of New Salem men pushed out from the mill. On the shore was a growing crowd of people, some from New Salem village, some who had come to have grist ground at the Rutledge-Camron mill and were on hand for the excitement.

"My, they sure are in a fix," they all declared, but no one had any idea about how to get the flatboat off the dam. The frightened hogs were blowing and squealing; boys were shouting on the bank; everyone crowded to the water's edge or waded out on the dam, while the flatboat quietly settled deeper in the water.

Presently willing hands from New Salem helped tote hundreds of barrels and boxes out of the cabin, and, under Abe's direction, loaded them in the ferryboat, which took them to shore. There they were unloaded and Jack and Billy stood guard.

The hogs unwillingly were pushed onto the ferry and even more unwillingly were taken off on the muddy shore. Each one, tethered by the hind leg to a tree, was squealing blue blazes.

Billy got a long stick and kept off the dogs.

By the time all this was accomplished, the spring sun had set behind the New Salem hill and the river slid over the dam in a chill purple shadow. It was getting dark and in the April dusk the frogs shrilled loudly from the swamps.

"Boys," said Abe with regret, "it's getting too late to shove her off tonight. We'll have to leave her like this till morning."

"You goin' to go off and leave Mr. Offutt's cargo all alone on shore? If them Clary's Grove boys find out about it, there'll be nary hog nor barr'l left, come mornin'," Sam Hill said doubtfully.

"Them squatters in the Pecan Bottoms, them that lives mostly on punkins 'cause they's too lazy to farm—if'n they hears about it—and they most likely have already—you won't have a rind of bacon left to haul to New Orleans," added John Camron.

"We won't leave it alone," said Abe decidedly. "Think I'd risk that? No, sir. Jack and John, you stand guard here while Billy and I go up to the village for something to eat and to have a word with Mr. Offutt. Then we'll come back down and you go up. Sleep up there, if you want. Billy and I can stand guard, can't we, boy?"

"Think you can handle things without us?" John questioned doubtfully. "Might be trouble."

"We'll manage," said Abe with assurance. He was certain that John and Jack would prefer sleeping in New Salem that night. It might sweeten John's disposition if he did.

Billy Masters, who tried not to think of being packed off home tomorrow, was glad of any chance to stay longer around Abe.

In Rutledge's Tavern, at the top of the hill trail, Abe and Billy found Denton Offutt. He was feeling mighty good again.

He had had plenty to refresh himself at Clary's store on the ridge, had bet on a rousing cockfight and had won, and now, in an expansive mood, he was partaking of Mrs. Rutledge's good food at the tavern.

"Well, well, my boy," he said genially, "how are things goin' down at the boat? Sit down, sit down, have some supper while you're talkin'. Mighty good burgoo, I must say, Mrs. Rutledge. Give Mr. Lincoln a bowlful, and *Mr.* Masters, too. I tell you, Abe, this here New Salem is a first-rate place. I already got plans for us here, yes, sir. I'm going to build me a grocery store down near Clary's—give him a little competition, *ha-ha-ha!* —and you're goin' to come and clerk for me, hear that, boy?"

Denton Offutt certainly had improved his time. And not a barrel had he toted.

"Thanks, Mr. Offutt," said Abe quietly. "Don't mind if I do have some supper. And we'll talk about that proposition to clerk in your store later on. I wanted to let you know we'll be ready to go in the morning, sir. We've unloaded most of her cargo and will stand guard down there tonight."

"How did you get her off, boy?" asked Offutt carelessly. "She looked to me like she was stuck till Kingdom Come. I 'bout give her up and decided not to go to N'Orleans at all."

"That boat was shippin' a lot of water," spoke up James Rutledge. "How you goin' to get it out—it'll take you a week to bail her."

"Well," said Abe, pretending to think. He cast his eyes solemnly over the big fireplace and over the rafters hung with hams and dried apples, swiveled them searchingly back to James Rutledge and to Denton Offutt, and for a moment to Ann Rutledge, who stood listening behind her father's chair. "Well, I guess likely I'll just bore a hole in the bottom and let the water *run* out!"

"Why, why—" sputtered Denton Offutt, setting down his coffee cup so hard it slopped over on the checked tablecloth and caused Mrs. Rutledge to click her tongue. Ann ran to fetch something to mop up the mess.

"Why—if you bore a hole in the bottom, she'll fill up like a bait bucket. Abe Lincoln, if you wreck that boat—if she sinks in that blamed Sangamon—I'll skin you, I vow I will, and nail your hide to the barn door!

"Now, now, Mr. Offutt," soothed Abe, grinning at the disturbed little man. "I doubt if you could do that without help. Your boat will be as good as new tomorrow. Be sure you get down there in time to come along. We're leaving early."

CHAPTER TEN

ABE SAT DOWN and Billy Masters with him. Ann Rutledge, in her quiet way, brought bowls of burgoo and corn pone and coffee. There was even a dried-apple pie. When they had eaten, Abe hated to leave the pleasant warmth and sociability of the low raftered room where the rich smells of the burgoo and the apple pie still lingered. But Abe and Billy knew they could not stay. The door closed solidly behind them. They were in a dark world, lit only by the stars and by the wavering glow of the lantern as the two made their way through the village. The scent of wild plum trees somewhere along the near-by forest edge filled the air with fragrance. The trail went past Clary's grocery, where lamps still burned and men were drinking and arguing, then led the two down the ridge to the bottoms where the mill stood silent and black against the river.

Abe was sure they'd find John and Jack either starved to death or scared to death, he wasn't sure which it would be. But they found the two suffering from neither affliction. Some of the village boys were there with them and they had made a comfortable fire which cast a ruddy, flickering glow over the piles of boxes and barrels. The hogs were quiet: too quiet. Abe commented on that strange fact.

"Sure, they're quiet. We turned 'em loose to root," said Jack Johnston.

"Hey, why in tarnation did you let those hogs loose?" shouted Abe. "We'll never get 'em back in time to go early tomorrow. I can't step up the hill for an hour without you fellows letting hogs loose and who knows what else! What else have you done?"

"We ain't done nothin'," said John Hanks sullenly. "Don't you go orderin' me around, Abe Lincoln, or I'll tell Tom Lincoln enough to git you thrashed within an inch of your life, big as you air. We let them blamed hogs loose to root because their snortin' and squealin' and carryin' on was drivin' us crazy. They'll come back. Scatter some corn tomorrow and they'll come a-runnin'."

Abe said nothing. His cousin and stepbrother rose and stretched. "Maybe we better come back after we've eaten," Jack suggested, with a look at all the barrels and boxes. "You'd have a time by yourselves if anybody started trouble."

"Come on, Jack," said John impatiently. "Abe thinks he can handle anything, and if he's so sure, let him. I for one will welcome a bed to sleep in tonight!"

Billy Masters and Abe were alone along the river. Dimly in the faint river-shine they could see the massive bulk of the boat. The frogs were racketing and the whippoorwills all but drowned out human conversation.

"You scared of them there whip-o-wills?" asked Billy, staring into the fire and hugging his knees.

"No, not me," said Abe. "Birds can't hurt a man. That's just talk. Now, Billy," Abe went on in a different tone. "We've got a long night ahead of us. Both of us daren't go to sleep at once. One of us has just got to keep his eyes peeled for the Clary's Grove boys or anyone else, Injun, bear, or white man, who tries to take our cargo or get on that boat. I wish to land they hadn't let those hogs run. No telling how many'll be lost by morning. There's likely catamounts in these woods; country's hilly enough. I'd hate to think of what one of those varmints could do to those hogs!"

An hour passed. Two hours. Billy began imagining sounds of approaching danger. A twig snapped; there came a low grunt— only a pig. A sudden splash in the river—probably a carp feeling the springtime, he reassured himself. A rustling in the dead leaves close by—and when a little deer mouse came skipping into the glow of the fire, Billy's eyes met Abe's smiling at him, and he grinned sheepishly. Both knew what the other was thinking; danger in the form of a mouse wasn't much to let yourself be scared of.

The stars over the river sparkled in a deep black sky. Billy and Abe talked about a lot of things. Abe told about the trip to New Orleans with Allen Gentry, and about how old Ahab Littleford knew Grandpappy Lincoln on the Wilderness Road, and about the Winter of the Deep Snow, and if the legislature ever would move the capital from Vandalia to a spot more central in the state.

"Now, New Salem'd be a fine location for the capital, with river traffic right up to the doorstep, so to speak, and plenty of land to expand to the west where it's level prairie."

"Sangamo Town would be, too," put in Billy, bound to bring excitement to himself, if he was not going to be allowed to go after it elsewhere.

"Yes, or Springfield, but it's a terribly muddy place in spring and terribly dusty, I hear tell, in summer. River isn't close enough, either. No, I doubt that they'd ever move it to Springfield."

They talked all around the subject which both were afraid to mention, but Billy at last broke a silence with, "Abe, why cain't I go with you? I just *got* to go!"

Abe, who knew it would come sooner or later, sighed and put his hand on the boy's knee.

"Billy," he said sadly, "your mother didn't want you to know because she didn't think you were man enough, but I think you are. You sure worked like a man today and I expect you to keep on being one. She says your daddy is very sick; he's likely not going to live long, and she wants you there so you can help while he's living and take his place when he's gone. There— I've told you. And I know you'll take it like a man!"

The boy stared into the fire. He swallowed and tried to say something, but the words wouldn't come. Two hot tears rolled down his cheeks, and he impatiently brushed them away with his hand. Abe just patted him gently on the knee.

"I'll—I'll—stay, Abe," Billy Masters whispered. "I—just didn't know."

The two sat without words and stared into the flames. Night in its spring freshness moved softly around them.

"Listen, Abe!" Billy whispered suddenly. "I hear somethin'."

Abe listened. It was very dark. Then he could see a little light glimmering fitfully down the dark hillside, heard low voices. He stiffened, waiting. He grasped a club and Billy picked up a stone.

The light bobbed nearer, nearer, and after what seemed like an age of suspense, the watchers could make out two figures. They were, of all things, two women.

"Why, Mrs. Rutledge, ma'am, and Miss Ann!" cried Abe, yanking off his hat. "What brings you down here so late, ma'am? Is there trouble up at the Tavern?" Billy just stared.

Mrs. Rutledge carried a little basket covered with a napkin.

"No, there's no trouble," she said in her gentle Southern voice. "But we—Ann and I—thought you might be hungry in your all-night vigil, so we brought you some biscuits and sliced ham, and some apple pie. I do hope you won't get the ague down here in the night air. It's so dreadful damp!"

Ann looked shyly at Abe and at Billy. "If you need help," she said, "just holler, my paw said. He and my brothers will come a-runnin'!"

Abe laughed.

"Thank you kindly, Miss Ann, and Mrs. Rutledge, too. We sure are beholden to you for your kindness, but I doubt if we'll need help. It's mighty quiet down here, barring the frogs, of course."

When Mrs. Rutledge and Ann had gone, Abe looked thoughtfully into the fire. "There are two fine ladies," he said, more to the fire than to Billy, who was munching at a biscuit. "In spite of the fact they're out here in the backwoods, they're real ladies. I lay you couldn't find finer ones anywhere."

"They're from Carolina," put in Billy, his mouth full. "Maybe that accounts for it. I hear tell that ladies are like that in the South. And, my land, think of them walkin' way down here to the bottoms, alone at night, like that. They didn't look scared, either."

Hours went by. A late-looking moon got up blearily over the river maples and put a little glimmer on the silken water. The hulk of the boat looked blacker than ever.

Billy was asleep. Abe looked into the fire and thought a lot of things he couldn't have put into words. He ate his piece of dried-apple pie and wiped the crumbs off his mouth with the back of his hand. Then he heard another little sound.

His heart thudding, he sat quietly and listened. The noise came again—the muffled jingle of harness, the squeak of leather, the soft-stepping splosh of horses' hoofs on the mud of the river road, somewhere near the mill. He could see nothing, no lights, nothing. But the sounds were there, and the skin prickled on the back of his neck.

He touched Billy's shoulder and the boy woke with a start. Abe laid a finger on his lips. The two crouched and slid over into the darkness so they wouldn't have the fire-shine in their eyes and wouldn't be silhouetted against the fire for anyone to see and maybe shoot at.

There were low voices, a faint rustling in the brush. Grasping his club and wishing he had a gun, Abe stood up with Billy beside him. The boy was shaking all over but he gripped a stone in each hand, ready to throw.

Then bedlam broke loose. There was an explosion of snorting and squealing and grunting, the terrified whinny of a horse, the thud of a body falling, the roar of a gun shot, and men's rough voices cursing loud enough to waken everyone in New Salem.

"Gosh blamed hogs!" cried a man's voice. "Didn't see the confounded critters till I stepped plumb on one!" Abe leaped like a long-legged panther in the direction of the sound, and just outside the circle of light cast by the fire he ran into a man scrambling to his feet. He gave him a push with one hand and the man went down, but as he tumbled he grabbed Abe by the legs and Abe fell on top of him.

The man was biting and clawing like a catamount. Abe felt a knee in his stomach and all but lost his breath before he twisted the fellow's brawny arms back until he yelled and let up on the pressure of his knee. Abe was panting, but his iron muscles held the man down while slowly he got to his knees, regained his balance—and then went over backward as the man lifted both feet and kicked with all his strength.

With a sickening gasp, Abe felt all the breath leave his body. He fell hard on the ground and his head crashed against a knobby tree root.

When Abe opened his eyes, Billy was raining tears on his face and trying to rouse him. Abe blinked and sat up gingerly. There was a bump on the back of his head and his middle felt as if he'd been butted by a billy goat, but otherwise he was all right. Then a sudden realization of what had happened flashed through his foggy brain and with an exclamation of alarm he leaped to his feet.

"The cargo, Billy! Did they get the cargo?" He whirled and raced to the circle of light where the fire still burned placidly. Everything looked just as he had left it a few minutes before, when the attack started.

"The hogs scared 'em off, whoever they were," said Billy with deep thankfulness in his heart as he saw Abe was all right. "After you started in on that feller that knocked you down, the others were scatterin' through the woods when they stumbled over more of them blamed pigs. I guess it rattled 'em so, they cleared out fast and the feller that jumped you was right after 'em. Never came near the cargo!"

There was a sound of retreating horses somewhere up the river road. Then a new clatter broke loose on the hill trail where lanterns came bobbing down the slope. Abe and Billy were standing with their backs to the fire when James Rutledge and his stalwart sons arrived. More lights followed. Sam Hill and Martin Waddell, the hatter, and Peter Lukins and Doctor Allen were there, nightshirts hastily rammed into pants.

"Who was it?" cried James Rutledge. "Heard the noise and a gunshot—anybody hurt? You all right, Abe Lincoln?"

With a wry grimace, Abe rubbed the back of his head. "Nobody was shot, sir. Gun went off by accident, I guess, when our visitors fell over the hogs. I've got an egg on the back of my head that would do credit to a goose, and I reckon some other fellow will have a couple of aches by morning. But we're all right, sir, and thanks for coming to help."

The men from New Salem scattered out through the trees. They found no one lurking there, no horses, but there was a gun lying on the ground among a lot of hog tracks, and there were trampled footprints of horses.

"We'll stay with you till morning," decided James Rutledge, putting more wood on the fire. "In a way we are responsible for the safety of your goods. Won't be long till light, anyhow. It's mighty late. Only the Clary's Grove boys'd be out so late. Lucky they tangled with the hogs. Those boys are tough customers and likely drunk to boot. They most generally are."

Abe's head was hurting like fury and he was glad to have someone else there to help guard Mr. Offutt's precious barrels. He would be heartily glad to get them reloaded and be on his way to New Orleans before anything else happened.

The party settled down around the fire and, although he vowed not to do so, Billy soon fell asleep again. The men talked a bit and some dozed. Once Abe thought he heard a sound out by the boat, but when he got up to see, it was only a deer swimming across the Sangamon. The morning star had risen in the east and shone so brilliantly that its light made a long path of glitter on the black flowing water.

And so the night passed and morning seeped grayly along the river.

CHAPTER ELEVEN

Early mists hung over the river and moved like wraiths through the trees. The Sangamon smell was there—damp, strange, pungent, a little fetid, a little sweet, a smell at once aromatic and unforgettable.

Abe yawned and poked up the fire. The others were all asleep. The sun was not yet up but a redbird in the tip of a maple whistled blithely to herald its coming. James Rutledge awoke and stretched. His boys stirred and opened their eyes. Billy was awake, too. All the menace of the night was gone. Somehow in the peaceful morning it seemed a little foolish to have been so concerned. But Abe's head still felt sore and his muscles ached from the impact of the hard blows. Still, whoever had tried to rob Mr. Offutt's cargo had not tried it a second time.

The hogs were awake long since and rooting for their breakfasts. Abe got a basket of corn for them, and, snuffling and grunting, they came trotting up. The Rutledge boys and Billy Masters slipped among them and tied a noose around each one's hind leg.

"How many you got, Billy?" called Abe, busy making coffee and frying bacon to go with the left-over biscuits from last night.

59

"Three's missin'," reported Billy after a quick count. "They shouldn't be far, less'n the Clary's Grove boys got 'em, which I doubt."

Billy ranged out through the woods. He found one unconcerned old sow busily eating a mess of mushrooms beside a stump, and, with all her bulk, she dodged livelier than he would have thought possible. When he crept in to slip a noose on her leg, she wheeled and her little red eyes looked downright wicked, her tushes long and sharp.

"*Come* on, girl, so-o-o-o, girl, I won't hurt you." He held out an ear of corn and the old sow pricked her ears forward and snuffled with her muddy snout, a mushroom dangling from the corner of her mouth. She moved a step or two closer. Billy let her take the ear from his hand, and in the same movement he dropped the rope over her head. The loop tightened as the sow snorted, dropped the corn, and tore off like a freight train through the forest. Billy, hanging on for dear life, was nearly yanked off his feet by his captive. The sow raced among wild gooseberry bushes and through a tangle of trumpet vines and wild grapes, heading straight for the river. Then she swerved, dragging Billy into the mud as he slid to his knees. Whereupon the sow snorted like fury and headed for her kinfolk around the corn. Billy tied her up securely and went back to look for his hat. The Rutledge boys, meanwhile, had found a missing shoat. One more was still unaccounted for.

"If we don't find that blamed hog, Mr. Offutt'll never let us forget it. I can hear him now," groaned Abe. "You boys see if you can find it, will you?" He turned to the New Salem boys who had come down from the village to see what was going on. "Billy, you go up to Henry Onstott, the cooper—he's down near the west end of Main Street, on the left, and borrow the biggest auger he has. Don't stay any longer'n you can help, boy. And tell Jack and John to come down; I need them."

Billy Masters was off on a run. He sprinted up the hill trail and along the village street until he located the cooper shop. Henry Onstott wasn't there, but Billy found him at his home, polishing off breakfast before joining most of the people of the village at the water front.

"Mr. Lincoln wants the borry of your biggest auger," Billy panted. "He'll be careful of it and return it right away."

Henry Onstott was more than willing to loan the auger, and not a little curious.

"What in time does Abe Lincoln want with an auger, boy? Can't see no possible place on a boat that needs an auger." Henry Onstott was clearly puzzled.

"Don't know myself, Mr. Onstott," said Billy importantly. "Abe said I should come back fast with it. You better come, too, Mr. Onstott. I 'low it's goin' to be excitin', gettin' that big boat a-floatin' again!"

As he passed the tavern, Billy met Jack and John just coming out. "Abe wants you right away!" Billy called to them and then trotted back down the hill. Halfway down he heard a snuffling in the underbrush and angled off the trail to investigate. He spied the third delinquent hog, nose down in the soft woods earth. Slipping up behind it, he got it tethered by the hind leg before the animal knew what was happening.

John Hanks and Jack Johnston caught up with Billy on the trail as the boy, with the auger and the hog, hurried triumphantly back to Abe Lincoln. They found him casually whittling a stick of maple a couple of inches thick. Billy stopped stock still. What would Abe be doing *that* for? Busy as he was, ordering everyone about to hurry, hurry, here Abe sat, whittling on a stick.

"Here's the auger, Abe," Billy said disapprovingly. "And I found that other hog. She was up on the hill, rootin' under the bushes. Abe, what you want the auger for?"

Abe took the auger. He knew a good show when he saw one. This one was neatly in the palm of his hand. Now Abe rolled his pants legs up high, and, with the auger and the stick of maple, waded out on the dam to the boat, went aboard, and disappeared in the cabin.

For what seemed a long time, nobody heard anything. Billy grew fidgety. What if Abe had hurt himself and nobody went in to find him . . . what if, what if . . . And then he could hardly believe what he was seeing when, right then and there, the big flatboat slowly and magnificently rose from her dismal posture in the river. As she got up and lay almost level on the dam, with her nose slanting downward, just a little, everyone could see water draining out of the bow. Abe, grinning all over his thin brown face, appeared in the hatch and climbed up on the cabin roof. Billy threw his hat into the air and whooped, and the men on shore roared a cheer that startled Denton Offutt, who was on his belated way down the hill trail to the river.

"How'd you do it, Abe?" shouted James Rutledge. Even on such short acquaintance, most of New Salem was calling him Abe.

"Like I told you last night," Abe shouted back. "Bored a hole in the bottom, rolled a few barrels forward to tilt her the other way, and the water ran out. And she just rose up like a lady!" answered Abe, still grinning. "Now I'll go below and plug her up, soon's the water is all out." He went below again and thrust the stick of whittled maple into the hole. The stick was still too stout, so he whittled it some more, smoothly and neatly all around, and tried again as the last of the water drained out. The plug was just right. He thrust it in and pounded it down tightly. The water would tighten it even more.

The boat was still on the dam, but she was setting lighter and higher, and occasionally she gave a little nudge forward, as if she was anxious to go, as anxious as Abe. Then Abe called for help and soon the dam was full of bare-legged men. And somehow, with Abe directing the effort and doing most of the work himself, the big flatboat eased gracefully over the dam and lay quietly in the water below.

Abe felt within himself a glorious sense of accomplishment. He had done it! He had got his boat safely over the obstruction that had threatened to thwart the whole wonderful journey to the South. Suddenly New Orleans seemed very near.

But there was a job still to do before they could be on their way. There was all that cargo to reload, all those ornery hogs to be persuaded back onto the ferry and pushed unwillingly onto the flatboat. Abe wiped the perspiration out of his eyes and shoved the next hog into the pen.

One by one they got the animals aboard. One by one the hundreds of barrels and boxes were heaved back in place. It was time to go.

Abe took Billy Masters aside.

"Billy," he said soberly, gazing down at him and feeling mighty sorry for the hurt in the boy's eyes, "Billy, you've got to start home now. Mr. Rutledge is going that way this morning and you can ride with him. You go home and be glad you can be of help and comfort to your mother, and when your time comes to go places, you'll be ready. Good-bye, Billy. I'll see you when I come back."

As Abe stepped into the skiff to return to the boat, Billy

could only watch him. He could say nothing because his throat was all filled up with grief.

Billy Masters stood on the bank of the muddy Sangamon and watched how they untied the big, beautiful flatboat that was held together with his own handmade oak pegs, saw how the boat moved away gladly on the current, and picked up speed as she went. The sail that Billy's mother had given Abe bellied out in the breeze. Everyone on shore waved and shouted loud farewells. Abe Lincoln and John Hanks and Jack Johnston waved their hats and yelled their good-byes. Denton Offutt waved with both plump hands and blew kisses to the girls.

"Good-bye, good-bye," he bellowed. "We'll be back soon. Comin' back to put a little life into New Salem, yes-sir-ree! Abe's comin' with me, too—" Off went the flatboat around the bend. Billy couldn't even see the river for the blurring in his eyes.

CHAPTER TWELVE

As he felt the boat sweeping along like the fine craft she was, freed from the shackles which had held her so rudely on the dam, Abe's heart swelled. He felt a great freedom, too, a release which was sweeping him and his boat on to adventure at last.

The river made a big curve, passed the few houses at Petersburg, then moved out into the sand country. This was different terrain. Abe had never seen curious, conical sand hills like these, hills with patches of orange puccoon brightening them and bird-foot violets by the acre blooming under a bright spring sun.

"I hear tell that them there hills all got Injuns buried on 'em," commented Denton Offutt. "Frank Gorsey, he plowed up a mess of old bones last spring, and a lot of stone axes and arrerheads and sich."

Abe looked at the sand hills, and his vivid imagination took hold of what Mr. Offutt had just said. At once he envisioned this place long ago, when Indians came in procession with their dead and buried them on the summits of the hills.

John Hanks lay on his back and stared at the sky. He cared nothing about the changing landscape. He was thinking of his family and about how he must find a better place for them to live before another winter came. A winter like the past one would be too much for flesh and blood to endure a second time. John's thoughts were mulling over the best way to escape from this disagreeable flatboat trip, how best to approach the difficult subject with Abe, who was justifiably touchy about it.

Jack Johnston went to sleep. Denton Offutt wished he had a drink and lumbered below to take a pull from the jug of applejack he'd thoughtfully provided. Abe rested on the steering oar and his hot, heavy eyes, eager for the sleep they had missed all the night before, watched the country slide past.

The voyagers stopped at Squire Godbey's to take on more hogs which, with the usual porcine stubbornness, decided they didn't want to ride the river. But after an exasperating delay, they were shoved on at last, and once more the afternoon breeze pushed out the patched sail. People in the few cabins on the shore came out and waved to them, and Abe and his companions always waved back. It was a friendly feeling to be moving along a watery road and to be greeted by strangers beside the way.

Now the river grew broader and the forests were greater upon the sandy shores. Abe tied up the boat for the night. Next morning, out through the pecan forests went the boat and was swept suddenly and almost without warning into the current of the Illinois, River of the Illiniwek. In a moment she had righted herself and headed properly downstream, the way all flatboats must go if they are to get anywhere.

Abe had the feeling of having shrunk considerably, he and the flatboat. The eighty-foot craft had looked enormous to him in the narrow confines of the little Sangamon, where sometimes you could almost touch the willows on either side as the boat eased through. But the Illinois was so wide that the far shore looked thin and small and remote, and on this vast expanse of water the flatboat seemed to him suddenly to have become frail and at the mercy of all the winds and waves. He wondered if he had built her strong enough, but it was too late to do anything about that. They were on the Illinois at last and the strong current was sending them steadily southwest. An eagle coasted on an updraft and for a little way followed the boat, sunshine glistening on the noble white head and tail, on the dark wings spreading widely against the sky. Then the eagle veered, its shadow swept across Abe, and the flatboat went on alone.

On the long journey south, Abe, John, and Jack took turns at the steering oar, although it was Abe who usually did most of this and who took over when there were many snags or any danger threatened. John had had experience on Ohio River flatboats, but his disinterest in this trip made him of little real help. The three were allotted the daily chores of cooking and cleaning up after meals, sweeping off the deck, and folding the blankets after the night's sleep. Since Denton Offutt was the owner and boss, he was not obliged to do anything, so he spent his time in a relaxed position on deck, ate well, talked a good deal, and slept when he was bored.

Down the Illinois, Abe steered the boat toward the shacks on stilts which marked the river front of Beardstown. Farther away from the water he could see houses, a lot of them, real houses made of boards, not log cabins. He'd heard of Beardstown, that it had seven hundred people living there and even had a newspaper office. Compared with other towns he had known, Beardstown, in spite of its ramshackle water front with its shanties built high to keep out of the flood, looked mighty big and prosperous. The boat nudged up to the wharf where other flatboats were tied. The crew unloaded the hogs, and Abe, with thankfulness in his heart, saw them get off, reluctant as usual, but off. Denton Offutt collected his money for them and loaded on more cargo. Abe, Jack, and John hastily sluiced the hog pen with buckets of river water, scrubbed it out, and had the space ready for more barrels and boxes.

Hurriedly they made sure they had everything aboard and then were off again. John Hanks was mortified at the way people on the landing laughed at them.

"Peddlers, that's what they be!" a loud-voiced water-front lounger said pointedly. "Look at that sail, would you, and smell that hog pen. I'd hate to ride all the way to Newerleans in a hog pen, wouldn't you, Bill?" And as everyone laughed, John Hanks clenched his fists and wished he was anywhere but here. Jack Johnston flushed with embarrassment, but Abe didn't mind the laughing. He didn't see anything especially funny about the way they looked, but if it amused people, that was all right. He'd be ready enough himself to laugh if something funny came along. It was all in what kind of funny bone you had, and what tickled it.

When they got under way again, Denton Offutt felt too used up to do anything but sleep.

"I do admire the peace and quiet," he murmured as he dozed off. "Them hogs like to wore me down with their gruntin' day and night."

ABE LEAPED LIKE A LONG-LEGGED PANTHER IN THE DIRECTION OF THE
SOUND, AND JUST OUTSIDE THE CIRCLE OF LIGHT . . . HE RAN INTO A MAN

"WELL, SIR," ABE CONTINUED, "WHEN HE HEARD ALL THE RACKET AND
SMELLED ... BRIMSTONE ... THE CHIEF WALKED OUT ON THE CLIFF TOP ..."

CHAPTER THIRTEEN

THE FLATBOAT floated downstream by day and at night it was steered to shore, where the crew tied up firmly to a tree. A river at night was too darkly dangerous for a lumbering flatboat to travel blindly upon it.

When the travelers pulled over to the west shore one evening, it was nearly sundown. The blaze of a spring sunset lay, orange and gilt and flame and silver, in an apple-green sky behind black trees. Above the hills the evening planet pointed its light through the blaze until it, too, was gone, and twilight filled the sky.

Abe always liked this time of day. The long, watchful hours on the boat, when he had to be alert all the time for fear of running into a floating dead tree or snags in the water, was finished. Now it was pleasant to pull over to a dusky, deserted shore and stretch his legs on land.

Denton Offutt roused himself and brushed off his clothes; he took a drink of applejack to fortify himself until supper was ready and strolled up and down the shore to ease his legs. Jack Johnston pulled in the fishline which he had hung over the rear of the boat all day. He took off the string of channel cats which he had hooked from time to time and had strung by their gills in the water to keep them fresh. Jack set himself to gutting and skinning the fish, and yelped in sudden pain when he was snagged by a catfish fin. He sucked the finger until it stopped bleeding.

John Hanks gathered firewood and built a campfire on the shore. Abe got the coffeepot to boiling and baked a spider of fresh corn pone. When Jack's catfish were ready, Abe dipped them in corn meal and fried them in hot pork fat, and the aroma of cooking filled the evening air like a benediction of home.

As night came down over river and shore, the four adventurers sat around the fire and finished off the last of the fish, drank the last mug of coffee, and batted at mosquitoes which already were beginning to hum and nip. Nobody said anything much. They had said it all during the day, and even Abe was quiet now. In a little while, with one accord, they retired to the boat cabin and went to bed.

Denton Offutt snored. He outsnored even the frogs, and Abe became so irritated by the noise inside the cabin that he got up and poked Mr. Offutt unceremoniously in the chest. With an explosive snort, the offender rolled over and his breathing came more gently for a while. John finally got to sleep; Jack, his pale hair fallen over his forehead, had long since been slumbering peacefully.

Abe was hopelessly awake. He lay and listened to the water lapping at the boat, felt how the craft responded gently to the lapping by heaving up and down, up and down, as if she were breathing. He could hear the sounds of the river forest, which never slept at night. He raised up on one elbow, opened a window, and looked out. And he saw a deer, like a shadow, come down to the shore a few yards away from the boat to drink. A raccoon came humping into the glow of the dying fire, pulled at the fishbones that had been left there, and dragged them off into the darkness.

In the spring night the stars came down and swam in the river. It was like lying between two universes—to be floating among the stars, with stars sparkling in the sky itself and stars in that liquid sky which was the river. Abe had a curious sensation of being suspended among them. . . . Finally he slept.

Abe always sensed, even inside the dark cabin, that dawn was nearing and it was time to prepare for an early start. Denton Offutt groaned and tried to snatch a little more sleep before he was forced to get up and eat. Jack Johnston was up with Abe and out into the crisp, cool, misty morning. They doused their faces and hands in the river and let the air dry them. Jack combed his hair neatly and slicked it down with water; if he wanted to be especially spruce, he went to the trouble of heating water and shaving. Abe tried to be neat, too, and he kept himself clean— Sarah Lincoln had dinned that into him enough times for him to remember it always—but in spite of the combing, his unruly black locks always stood on end soon after he had smoothed them in place.

Abe stirred up the remaining coals of the dying fire and put on more wood. By the time he had breakfast ready, all the others were washed, combed, and ready to eat.

And then, by full sunrise, the boat was again on its way down the Illinois River.

They were on a highway of ancient travel, a watery road which held no imprints of voyagers nor any record of their passing. In the old days of exploration, the country was too rugged, too heavily forested, or too marshy for men to travel with any degree of ease or speed across it, so they took to the rivers. Down the Illinois came French priests and explorers—Marquette,

Jolliet, Hennepin, LaSalle, Tonti—and Indians and voyageurs and fur traders, centuries before Abraham Lincoln piloted a heavy freight boat down that same river.

Abe knew that the Illinois was widening downstream beyond the high green hills of the Military Lands, but there were so many willow swamps on either side that the craft came into an even mightier river before he realized what was happening. Suddenly a stronger current with half a continent behind it whirled the flatboat around, broadside in the Mississippi.

CHAPTER FOURTEEN

A̲BE WAS scared. He had lost control of the boat. As if she possessed a will of her own, the craft plunged and wallowed sideways while Abe and John battled to hold and turn the steering oar. Jack Johnston put his strength into it, too. The flatboat, however, was no longer controlled by men but by a river, and she paid no attention to the human muscles which pulled mightily at a long hickory toothpick. The flatboat simply would not turn. Instead, she was being carried awkwardly broadside on the galloping current of the Mississippi River.

By this time the mouth of the Illinois was hidden around a big bend of the Mississippi.

"Look out—look out!" squealed Denton Offutt who was clinging to the mast. A flood-ravaged dead tree full of branches, bounding along on the current, was heading for the plunging flatboat. The tree hit the boat a resounding blow, caught against her, and was carried along with her. The sail flapped futilely in the spring wind and the flatboat still would not be turned.

The hickory sweep groaned as if it knew Abe's own agony, and for a while he was afraid it would snap. If the steering oar broke, then indeed they would be at the mercy of the river. The current would carry the awkward, wallowing mass of

73

timber which was Abe Lincoln's carefully built flatboat, and
when the river got tired of tossing her about, it would deposit
her casually and permanently upon the nearest sand bar or
rock ledge or in a cove full of snags.

But now slowly, slowly, as Abe, John, and Jack braced themselves and pulled with all their strength, there came along the
fibers of the hickory sweep a sensation of resilience, of change,
of a final and graceful giving in. The boat at last was turning
. . . turning . . . but then the current mischievously caught
her again and once more she was wallowing while waves splashed
spray in the crew's faces and Denton Offutt's white face dripped
with tears and river water.

"Easy—easy!" gasped Abe, the cords standing out on his
neck and his mighty arms distended with muscles straining their
utmost. "Easy—she's coming. . . ." And slowly once more the
flatboat was resisting the river. Slowly she was turning, a little at
a time, sidling against the waves, nosing a bit farther into the
current instead of being slapped broadside by it. Slowly, slowly
she got her bow around, and when a puff of wind at that moment hit the sail, it swung the boat full into the current at last.

Perspiration ran off Abe's forehead. "Take it for a minute,
John," he gasped. The boat was all right now. The channel was
clear. John hadn't strained so hard; he could manage things for
a bit.

Abe dropped to the deck and lay there panting and letting
the life come back into his arms. After a while his heart quieted,
his body relaxed. He could feel strength seeping back into him.
It had seemed to him that all his power had drained down the
fibers of the hickory sweep, that the boat and the river were
going to show him who was master.

CHAPTER FIFTEEN

THE FLATBOAT from Sangamo Town was not alone on the great river. Never again on the long push south to New Orleans would she be alone as she had been most of the time on the Sangamon and on the Illinois. Abe and his boat had put themselves into the great stream of commerce, of history, of mankind. Here was the main artery of middle American travel and trade: here was the Father of Waters in the spring of 1831.

Abe Lincoln had a feeling for the Mississippi. It was one known by a lot of people, a feeling that this great, relentless river was part of the lifeblood of men and of a continent. To Abe, it was like coming home to be on its broad brown waters once again. He had never seen the ocean, but he believed that the affection some people had for the ocean must be similar to the way he felt about the old river. It was part of him. He could almost feel Mississippi River water running in his veins! There was nothing else like it, no river quite so exciting to look at and wonder about and live with.

He thought of all the men who had fought and died to own the Mississippi—as if anybody could own a river like this! But they'd tried, everyone from the King of Spain to the King of France, and the King of England, too, and that was not so very long ago, either, if he remembered right.

He'd read about how Napoleon sold the Mississippi, just like selling a piece of sidemeat over a counter. Napoleon had never seen the river; and because he'd never seen it, he could sell it cool as a cucumber and never bat an eye. Abe bet that if Napoleon had come by boat and had floated on the Mississippi just once, he'd never have wanted to let go of it. But he did let go of it, the Louisiana country and the Mississippi thrown in, and President Jefferson was lucky to get it at the figure he did. People had said that fifteen million dollars was a lot of money, but it was only about four cents an acre, when you figured the amount of land and water he bought with it.

"Where's the Mississippi start from?" Suddenly Jack broke into Abe's reverie. Jack was steering. The river was beginning to get him, too.

"Why, I don't rightly know," said Abe, puzzled. He had no answer to that question. He knew about De Soto discovering it long ago, and about how French priests had navigated it, and about LaSalle and the other Frenchmen who had had their troubles over the river when they tried to take it for the King of France. He knew, too, that the river belonged to America now, but he didn't know where the Mississippi began.

He was embarrassed not to have an answer, and puzzled, too. The others usually looked to him for an answer to most things, but they had him here.

"Jack, by time—I just don't know! I don't think anybody knows. They say it's up in the north, maybe in Canada, for all we know. Nobody's found its headwaters, but I reckon someone will. Likely the Indians know, but they haven't told anyone."

"I'd like to be the one to find it, wouldn't you, Abe?" mused Jack dreamily. Abe looked with approval at his kinsman. Jack was getting there. He was waking up a little. He'd never before had the imagination nor the gumption to *want* to do anything much, except feed himself, maybe, or make money without working, or stay close to the fire in cold weather. Even if it was such an unlikely thing as finding the headwaters of the Mississippi—Abe laughed silently to think of Jack Johnston ever getting up *that* much gumption—even if it was as far-fetched as that, it was good, anyway, that he'd even thought of it. Still, Abe wished he knew where the Mississippi began. It would plague him until he knew.

Right now his business was to pilot this loaded flatboat down to the end of the Mississippi, not go adventuring up north to find its headwaters. He and the flatboat were part of an almost continuous line of freight carriers moving down the Mississippi, a great wet stream of commerce all heading south.

Downstream, the river grew more powerful and more muddy as streams along the way poured silt into it. There was a huge-ness, a terrible, awe-inspiring majesty, as the brown waters moved strongly southward past limestone bluffs, past towering white cliffs which stood above the eastern shore.

If Abe felt that he and the flatboat had lost stature when they entered the Illinois, they were dwarfed and puny below those cliffs and upon the smoothly flowing waters of the Missis-sippi.

CHAPTER SIXTEEN

Tall above the river towered strange, dazzlingly white cliffs. Not as a straight white wall, but as a great stony undulation; there were canyons here, outthrusts there, or massive pillars with huge rocks balanced on their tops. It was a lonely shore, a mysterious and exciting one.

"Hey, look at that!" Jack Johnston exclaimed. Denton Offutt rolled over and blinked, and John Hanks stared, too, and whistled. Abe rested the oar and gazed at the cliffs. There, distinctly enough, were the paintings of two huge winged creatures. They showed the marks of weathering, but the forms of the creatures were distinct and clearly visible in the bright spring sunshine.

Three years earlier, Abe had listened to an old riverman downstream telling about Indian paintings of the Piasa Bird on white bluffs near Alton, and these must be the very ones the old man had been talking about. Rivermen generally stretched the truth a mite, but the paintings at least were just as they had been described.

"An old man told me about those pictures," began Abe. "He said that long ago, during the time of the Illinois, or maybe even before, there was a monster bird called the Piasa which lived in that high cave back there near Grafton. The critter flew about the countryside catching and eating Injuns.

"By and by," Abe went on, "the old chief, Ouatoga, couldn't stand seeing his people eaten; he was losing half his tribe that way. So he up and had himself a dream, and when he woke he knew just what to do. So," Abe continued, "the chief picked out six of his best archers and told 'em to get their sharpest arrows and dip 'em in poison. Don't know what kind of poison, but some kind they had then, real deadly. He told the warriors to hide in the bushes up top of one of these cliffs, right up there, maybe." Abe flung one bony hand toward the white cliffs to his left, where swallows wheeled in the sunshine.

"He got them all set by sunrise. That was the time of day when the Piasa got to roaming about to find its breakfast. Pretty soon, what did they hear but a roaring sound and a thundering and a flashing like lightning, even though the morning was clear. Then down the river came flying a great huge critter—wings of a bat, they said, face of a man, horns of a deer, claws like an eagle's, tail like a fish, so long it flapped 'way out in the air as the critter flew."

The others hung on his words. That Abe—he could really spin a tale to hold a man.

"Well, sir," Abe continued, "when he heard all the racket and smelled fire and brimstone on the critter's breath, the chief walked out on the cliff top, all alone, and waited for the Piasa Bird to come down and grab him. Only he hoped it would work out as his dream said, and he wouldn't be grabbed by those great sharp claws that were big as a hay-rake, likely.

"The big wings flapped down. With a horrid scream, the Piasa ju-u-u-st was about to grab him, when the archers in the bushes let go their arrows, and *bing!* the thing was hit!" Abe paused a long moment as the river slid past and the sun made water shadows on the cliffs. By this time the flatboat had passed the paintings. "The Piasa screamed and it smoked, and it went rolling and flapping over the edge of the cliff and fell into the water.

"Well," Abe went on—as usual relishing the story as much as his listeners did, perhaps more—"that was the end of the Piasa Bird, as they called it. They never saw it again, hide *nor* hair. But a few years later the Injuns painted two pictures up there on the rocks, to remember the Piasa by, I guess. For a long time, all the Injuns passing here either shot arrows at the pictures, or rifle balls. They say the ledges are littered with 'em."

And as the boat moved downstream, the pictures, illuminated now with the fine, bright glow of a tale out of the far past, were finally lost to view in the blue mists of the river.

CHAPTER SEVENTEEN

With some inner puzzlement, Abe Lincoln had noticed how John Hanks seemed to grow more cheerful after they passed the Piasa cliffs. John's discontent and his ill-concealed revolt against his kinsman's position of importance on the boat had not been lost upon Abe. As pilot and builder, he could say what had to be said, could order the others to do what needed to be done. But because John was the older, that in itself was enough to make him boil when he was told to do something—take over the steering oar, dump out the garbage, sweep off the deck. It didn't matter what it was; John always resented it. Ever since he had rashly been persuaded into joining the expedition, he had regretted it; his regret only increased as the watery miles lengthened between him and home. More and more, he had refused to take orders; he had sulked for some miles until the river broadened as the white cliffs vanished in the distance. At this point Abe saw John visibly brighten. Cousin John was, in fact, more amiable than he had been since the journey began. And Abe, with a sense of foreboding, watched to see what would come next.

When the smokes of St. Louis rose in the distance, John cleared his throat, swallowed, stood up, and faced his cousin.

"Abe," he began awkwardly, "I want you should pull over to St. Louis and let me off. I can't go no farther. I got to go home. I hate the river and you know it—you ain't made it any easier, either, the way you been navigatin' this scow into trouble! You'll git along a whole lot better without me and so will I." John looked down at his work-hardened, calloused hands. "I just got to go home," he said in a lower tone. On top of everything else, Abe suddenly saw stark homesickness in John Hanks's face.

"We need you, John," began Abe, wondering how best to say what he had to say. "I wanted you to come along because it looked like a pretty good trip and you'd make money at it, too. You had enough experience on the Ohio to be good at navigating on the Mississippi. But I see it hasn't worked out. If we'd started in March, like we planned, maybe it would have been different. As it is, we got delayed a month and that's soured you on everything else. You haven't been happy any of the time, and you only make everyone else miserable with your eternal complaining. So I guess it's best if you want to go. We'll miss you, John, and I hope you don't regret leaving."

"Why not come with me?" suggested John with a sudden crafty look in his gray eyes. "You, Jack—your mother'll be mighty lonesome for the sight of you. Why don't you come, too? Abe here's so high and mighty, *he* kin sail a boat singlehanded all the way to New Orleans. *He* don't need you."

Now the full impact of John's discontent flashed upon Abe. John was determined to break up this voyage. If Jack Johnston left, too, Abe would be hard put to do as John had suggested so sneeringly—sail the flatboat singlehanded to New Orleans. It would be a risk to take on new hands at any place they stopped; you never knew about rivermen, whether they were good or bad, or would murder you in your sleep. Mr. Offutt was not much use as a crew member. There would be only Abe to man the sweep all day long, watch out for snags and sand bars as the going grew more dangerous downstream. He could manage without John, but if Jack went— Once more Abe saw the expedition dissolving before his eyes. Maybe Denton Offutt saw it, too, because he spoke up plaintively.

"Now, John, don't you go to takin' my crew away. You stay with us, Jack. Abe needs you. You cain't desert like this. It's— it's mutiny!"

Abe smiled wryly at this nautical term and wondered briefly where Mr. Offutt ran onto such a word at such a time. But mutiny, that's what it was and John was doing it.

Abe looked at Jack Johnston, who had slicked himself up and was neatly shaved so he would present a good appearance in St. Louis. Sarah Lincoln always prided herself on her son's appearance, but Tom Lincoln harshly called him a dude and thought up the dirtiest of jobs so that Jack would lose some of that cleanness and neatness which were his pride. He had listened closely to the argument flowing back and forth across the deck. Now he spoke up.

"Oh, shut up, John," he said plainly, pouring his shaving water over the side and wiping out the basin. "I ain't leavin' this boat till she gets to New Orleans and they tear her apart for stove wood. Maybe you ain't havin' fun, but I'm havin' a wonderful time! No wood to chop, no rails to split, no fields to plow—by golly, I like it here and I'm stayin'! If I was home, Paw would be workin' the livin' daylights out of me. You go if you want; we kin do without you, I guess. But not me. I stay!"

Abe felt a vast relief somewhere around the region of his stomach. Denton Offutt patted Jack's shoulder and retired to the cabin for a little refreshment. John Hanks glumly went below to

83

gather up his few effects in a small carpetbag. While he was in the cabin Denton Offutt paid him what was coming to him, and at the same time felt a certain relief that John was leaving. Just one less to pay when they landed at New Orleans.

Abe nosed the flatboat toward the shore and she settled into a berth on the crowded, bustling, noisy St. Louis water front. Lined up there with the flatboat from the Sangamon were dozens of steamboats—how Abe admired the steamboats!— packets, keelboats, pirogues, and flatboats loaded with northern furs. And there the crew said good-bye to John Hanks. John was not profuse with his farewells.

"I sure hope you don't regret not comin' home with me, Jack," he said sourly. "I'll tell your maw you had a chanct to come home and wouldn't do it!"

"Good-bye, John," said Abe firmly, and they shoved off before Jack had an opportunity to change his mind. Abe doubted if he would have gone with John. The lure of adventure down South was enough to make Jack Johnston even tackle a job of work if it was necessary to get him there.

And the job was waiting for him as soon as the flatboat got out in the current. Never again on the long trip down the river would the flatboat's crew be able to forget the river and its menaces. Watching and steering—that was the job that lay ahead for lazy Jack Johnston and his more energetic stepbrother, Abe Lincoln.

The flatboat, gathered up on the great surge of the Mississippi, floated downstream like an Illinois oakleaf. It passed the flood of the Missouri which dumped its yellow waters into the greater river.

The Missouri had come twisting and turning across the country from eight thousand feet up in Montana, where mountain snows and tumbling alpine streams fed it, down through the Bear Paws, into the Dakotas, other streams along the way adding size and color. The Marias and the Musselshell, the Big Horn and the Powder River, the Yellowstone bringing color from the paint country, all helped make the Missouri. It moved on through Indian territory, through plains and badlands. Here came the Cheyenne and the North Platte, the Niobrara from Nebraska, on, on, past the Indian encampment where Omaha later grew up . . . here came the Solomon, here came the Kansas. And across the Missouri country to St. Louis, the river flowed to the meeting place of waters.

Yellow mud, essence of the West . . . flavored with sage and buffalo grass, water which had mirrored bison herds that by millions had drunk of the yellow waters . . . had mirrored Indian faces that had looked into it . . . water thickened with silt from all the lands it had traveled through, poured now into the Mississippi.

Navigating a flatboat with a valuable cargo on the Mississippi did not mean merely to let the boat drift with the casual current—not on Ole Mississipp' which changed its mind and its channel from year to year and even from day to day. Sand bars that were there two years ago might be inland by now. Snags that were there now might have fallen in a week ago, or only that very morning, and could wreck a boat or delay a voyage. Islands rose after every flood; channels were cut across the endless meandering bends to make new and uncharted bends.

And it required constant attention on the part of Abe and Jack, and even from Mr. Offutt, to watch not only the river's unpredictable character but the other craft which used it for a highway. The three from Illinois had to be alert for rafts that had taken the bit in their teeth and were surging hell-for-leather south. There had to be endless caution for other flatboats and for the keelboats with their tough crews who itched to prove their valor.

There was nothing on the river tougher or more dangerous than a keelboatman spoiling for a fight. Abe had warned Jack not to provoke one of them; it wasn't worth it, not for any insult.

"Why, I've seen keelboatmen jump the crew of a flatboat for no reason at all, disable the men and take over the boat. You've got to watch out for them and don't do a thing that might set them off. Half-horse and half-alligator, they like to brag—half-crazy, I'd add to it. No sense to the way they act. It's the keelboatmen who give the river a bad name."

But everyone on the river, keelboatmen included, had to be wary of the steamboats that came puffing upstream in a very superior way with no trouble at all—steamboats still were a miracle after so many centuries of man's having to travel with the current or labor with human muscle against it. This was an uphill river for every craft but the steamboats.

At night when the flats were tied up to shore, usually in a group for protection against bandits, Abe liked to sit on deck and watch the steamboats passing by. Their lights were fluid gilt on the black satin water. Music and voices and laughter came from them, and there were the glorious flurries of red sparks which flung themselves skyward when the boilers were being stoked. And even though the Sangamon River flatboat had been a means of escape for Abe, had taken him out of the woods and away from the memory of the Winter of the Deep Snow, it was stodgy and slow and dull and one-track-minded in comparison with the elegant steamboats climbing upriver in the night.

By day, Abe's flatboat had to be guided endlessly around the snags. The Mississippi's unstable shores constantly gave up trees which fell in and were swept along on the current until they came to rest somewhere in the channel.

It was largely because of these snags in the untidy Mississippi that Abe had been hired to pilot Mr. Offutt's flatboat to the markets of New Orleans. Abe's other journey south with Allen Gentry had taught him what to expect—taught him never to take the Mississippi on its face value—for under its shining surface might lurk snags that would wreck the largest boat.

As they floated south, Abe told Jack what to look for.

"There are different kinds of snags, Jack," he said one beautiful morning when the Mississippi stretched away to the south in deceptive smoothness. "Those that come floating at you are least dangerous. You may get bumped, as we did when that tree hit us while we were broadside at the mouth of the Illinois, but you aren't likely to get wrecked." The memory of that experience when they entered the Mississippi still made Abe cringe inwardly at what might have happened.

"Now look over there," he went on, pointing to a dark object just thrusting above the water. "That's a sawyer. See how it sort of saws back and forth with the motion of the water? Well, you've got to watch out for sawyers; they're anchored in the mud, and if you run into one, you'll have a time getting off. But you can always see them moving back and forth in the water. Generally a sawyer isn't really big or it wouldn't be moving like that."

The boat floated on. Jack took his turn at the steering oar, but Abe sat down close by.

"Deadhead coming up," he said suddenly. "Steer over to the middle of the channel, boy. Watch it, watch it—" Abe leaped up and took the long sweep. He got the flatboat around the stiff stump of a snag which stood motionless in the moving water, then gave the oar back to Jack and sat down again.

"You've got to watch out for deadheads, Jack," he went on patiently. He began to doubt if his stepbrother ever would make a very good navigator. "Deadheads are fastened down in the mud—likely they're stumps of trees that grew there once—and they jar you considerably if you hit. But the sleepers are worst of all."

"What's a sleeper?" asked Jack in a bored voice. He wished he himself was sleeping, like lucky Mr. Offutt who, just because he was the owner of this flatboat, didn't have to take a spell with the oar.

"Sleepers—you can't see 'em, Jack. And they don't move. That's why they're so dangerous, and why you have to keep a constant watch. It's also why we can't travel at night. You can only guess at where a sleeper lies, just by the way the water runs over a certain place, or by a shadow, a ripple. And if you do run on one, your boat piles up on top like a steer on a fence post, and there you are."

The sun was warm. Abe's eyes were weary from watching the bright water with the rays upon it—always as they sailed south they had the sun in their eyes all day long. Jack was steering and keeping an indifferent watch over the conditions of the river. Abe fell asleep.

He woke with a start that brought him, cat-like, to his feet. He hadn't dreamed that sudden, low *crunch,* nor the immobility of the flatboat.

Jack was wildly flailing the steering oar. Most of the time he had it in the air, but when it dipped and splashed in the water, nothing happened. The boat was stuck.

"What did you do?" cried Abe, grabbing the oar. "Didn't you

watch for snags like I told you to?"

"It looked all right," defended Jack, scowling. "I didn't see no snags, and you needn't yell at me, Abe Lincoln. I didn't do it a-purpose!"

"No, no, of course you didn't," Abe admitted more peaceably, working desperately with the steering oar. "But just the same you've run us onto something. I should never have let you steer while I went to sleep. Here, help me with this. Maybe if both of us pull, we can move her one way or another till she slides off. Likely it's a sleeper you've rammed us on."

Jack pulled hard on the long sweep. Abe pulled. Denton Offutt watched, but did not offer to help. His pudgy white hands would have given little assistance and he knew it.

Around them surged the Mississippi. Two flatboats floated past. Men on board waved and shouted, and looked back, grinning, at the flatboat in distress which would not move. Abe began to feel more concern than he had at first. They were really stuck.

"I'm going down under and see what's holding us," he said finally, stripping off most of his clothes. He slid overboard—too dangerous to try a dive.

Taking a deep breath, he ducked under the hull of the big flatboat and groped with his hands in the shadowy water until they struck a slimy tree trunk. His breath was gone and his lungs were bursting as he came out from under the boat and sought air for a moment or two.

"See anythin'?" asked Jack, not too hopefully.

"No—but I—felt something," said Abe, taking deep gasps of clean spring air. "Dead tree down there. Don't know how big—must be plenty big to hold us—like that. I tell you, Jack, I don't know *how* we're going to get loose!"

He went under again. He didn't waste time in groping. He knew where the snag stood. His big hands followed cautiously up the topmost section to find where a big slime-covered bough held the boat fast. He found it . . . felt along the bottom of the boat. No break there, but the top of the snag was securely wedged against the boards. Air—air—and he bobbed out into the sunshine again and took deep, deep gulps of air before he went under a third time.

Now with his two powerful hands he grasped the snag and pulled, treading water the while, and just when his lungs were cracking again and the river current was dragging at him, he felt the snag give a little. Out he came for air, then back again in a hurry to take advantage of that little victory. With all his strength behind those massive shoulders, Abe Lincoln pulled back on the snag. Something broke, and suddenly the snag no longer was holding the boat.

Hurriedly Abe sprang for the sunny water and came to the surface in time to see the boat floating free again and heading serenely downstream without him. A few long strokes brought him back to the flatboat, where he scrambled on board.

He was still panting a little when he took the steering oar from the unprotesting Jack. Without a word they watched the smoothly flowing river.

After a bit Abe's face cleared and he began to grin. "Jack," he said, "when I was bobbing up and down in the water back there, it reminded me of my polite old uncle. He was the most mannerly member the family ever had, I hear. He made a trip on the Mississippi once, but the boat sank and he with it. Uncle got his head above the water, took off his hat, and said, 'Ladies and gentlemen, will you please excuse me?' and down he went for the last time!"

CHAPTER EIGHTEEN

At the tip of southern Illinois, the Ohio River poured its waters, which had come from as far east as New York State, into the great body of the Mississippi.

Below Cairo, the Mississippi twisted and turned in curves and bends. Abe could think only of the river. For long hours of daylight, he and Jack kept a close vigil over the current.

"Watch now," warned Abe as they went around a huge double bend, a great S, "Island Number Ten's in here somewhere, unless she's sunk as some do. No, there she is; watch now, we've got to stay in the channel."

"What's the town, Abe?" Denton Offutt murmured from his usual reclining position on the deck. He hardly ever looked at the towns they passed, but he felt he was doing his duty to inquire their names.

"New Madrid, Mr. Offutt," Abe answered promptly. "New Madrid, Missouri. That's the place where they had the earthquake. Let's see, 1811, if I recollect aright. They must have had a terrible time of it, those poor folk who lived here then. I heard a riverman tell about it three years ago when Allen and I stopped here."

"Tell us about it, Abe. I never heard of it before," urged

Jack, for whom Abe's endless fund of stories always lightened the tedium of the days. "What's an earthquake, anyway?"

"Well, seems like things began to shake and shiver early one morning in December," began Abe, resting on the long sweep. "People were shaken out of their beds and dishes fell out of the cupboards and smashed to flinders on the floors. Cows and hogs ran about bellowing and people were scared to death!

"That was only the beginning. Great spouts of mud and sand and water shot up through the cornfields, and tremendous cracks opened and swallowed men and cattle and whole houses, even, and closed again like the Trump o' Doom, and you'd never have known they were there, buried alive. The banks of the river caved in, and part of the town fell in with them, and the people drowned. Oh, it was awful! Land sank and lakes were made, just like the hand of God on the days of creation, only these were the days of destruction."

Jack Johnston was listening with his mouth open. Even Denton Offutt opened his eyes and sat up.

"Lots of people died," went on Abe mournfully. "And the river, gosh-a-mighty, I'm glad we aren't having an earthquake now! The river got all churned up and confused, and started turning back on itself. There were great waves that tore away the shores, cut across the bends, made new channels, and sure caused terrible havoc, I vow they did. Some steamboats sank. I reckon they're still down there with all hands on board, down in the mud somewhere, maybe just beneath us."

"How long did it last?" asked Denton Offutt in awe.

"Three months, near as I can recall what the riverman told me," went on Abe. "Things looked considerably different when the earthquakes were over. Not only were they felt awfully hard in Missouri and Tennessee, but I hear tell they felt 'em

92

clear east to Boston. And I remember Paw telling how it shook up Kentucky. I was just a baby and didn't know about it, but he said it scared Mother something awful, and I reckon Paw wasn't far behind!"

Abe steered the big flatboat over to the busy water front of New Madrid, Missouri, and slid into a berth for the night.

New Madrid had recovered from the disaster. It was like a busy seaport where a hundred or more boats arrived every day. Here flatboats usually stopped, and here many of their owners sold all their goods and the boats, too, and walked back home again. There were boats from all the places upstream along the Mississippi and the Illinois, the Missouri, and the Ohio—boats with Yankee trade goods from New England, come down from Pittsburgh; lumber from Pennsylvania and New York State; corn and apples and potatoes from Ohio; furs from the Northwest Territory; chickens and ducks and lead from Missouri; hogs and corn, whiskey and cider, and dried fruits from Illinois and Indiana; tobacco, hemp, and flour from Kentucky and Tennessee.

However, nothing would be disposed of from the Sangamo Town boat. Abe had only pulled it in for the night, for there was safety in numbers along this rowdy shore. Now the other rivermen, their trading done, were roaming from boat to boat to meet old friends or to pick a good rousing fight to top off the day. The water front was noisy with drinking and singing, fighting and laughing, gambling and trading. The boatmen were at it half the night, but they managed to get a little sleep before the bugles blew along the water front at dawn.

Abe and Jack guarded their boat while Mr. Offutt went out to get some liquid refreshment. At about ten that night there was considerable racketing somewhere up in the town on the bluff, the baying and awful tonguing of bloodhounds, men shouting. Abe and Jack, from their position on the flatboat deck, could see torches glimmering here and there in the darkness. Then the noise faded away in the distance.

"W-what was that?" shuddered Jack Johnston. The hounds made his flesh creep.

"Don't know," said Abe, wondering, "unless it's bloodhounds after a runaway slave. This is slave territory, I guess likely. Oh, that's an awful sound!"

Denton Offutt, who at a late hour finished having a sociable time with some new-found friends in a water-front saloon, came staggering back to the flatboat and Abe and Jack put him to bed. They locked the trap door and turned in, too.

Early the next morning, when the bugles blared and there was a great bustle of activity on the water front, the boats, one by one, cast off and were on their way in a great procession down the Mississippi.

CHAPTER NINETEEN

THE ILLINOIS flatboat was several miles downstream from New Madrid when Denton Offutt, as usual, went down into the cabin for his morning swig of applejack to give him strength until lunch time. He let out a whoop that brought Jack to the edge of the hatch to peer inside.

"Come down here quick!" Mr. Offutt sputtered. "Get Abe down here right away!" The little man was in a boiling fury. Abe gave over the steering oar to Jack and swung down into the cabin.

"Look what we got—a stowaway!" shrieked Denton Offutt. "Confounded runaway slave, that's what we got!" He yanked the canvas off some barrels and revealed behind them the frightened, panicky, dark brown face of a young Negro man who was trembling as if he had the shakes.

"*Please*, suh, *please*, suh, don't put me off, I beg of you-all. Gennelmen, lemme ride a ways with you-all!" And the tears rolled down his cheeks, leaving shiny streaks in the dust on them—all the way down to his blue shirt. There were red and purple welts across his neck and over one cheek.

"Come on out and talk to us," said Abe gently.

"Don't let anybody see me!" the stowaway begged. "If'n they

seen me, I'd be a goner sure. They was after me with the dogs las' night, suh, and I didn' know whar else to turn, so I slid in heah while de gennelmen was lookin' de other way." Denton Offutt glared at Abe and Jack. "Dey didn' follow me to de water front. I give dem de slip up on de hill and come down a little trail I knowed over de bluff. Oh, suh, I jist got to git away."

"Why?" asked Abe.

"Dey done sold my wife and chile, suh," the man said simply. "I tried to git away to whar dey's at, and if dey catch me in New Madrid now, dey'll sell me down to Newerleans, sure. My masta, he said so. I got away three days ago, but dey done caught me—you can see dey beaten me. But I done tried it again, and dey almost got me. Let me ride with you, please, suh."

"We ain't no slave runners," snarled Denton Offutt in an ugly tone which Abe had never heard from him before. "This here's a respectable freight boat and I ain't goin' to git mixed up with no slave runnin'! You got to git off and git off quick!" And he made a threatening gesture toward the man, who cringed down behind the barrels again.

"Listen, Mr. Offutt," said Abe soberly. "We can't do that. We can't do any less than what we'd want him to do for us if we were in the same fix. I think we ought to let him ride a piece and then let him get off wherever he thinks it's safest. They can't track him on the river, and with all those boats tied up at the town last night, they'd be hard put to it to search every one, if they could catch up with 'em, which they can't. I say let him stay. Where you want to get off, mister?" he asked the man.

"Anywhere on de other side," the man said humbly. "Anywheres but in Missouri or Arkansaw. Celine and little Cal, dey was took to Nashville, I hear. If'n I was to ride along and maybe

96

get off at Memphis, I'd be safe and could maybe get to whar dey at. Oh, suh, I thank you, and God will sho'ly reward you-all for yo' kindness." And the man wept again.

"Oh, shut up with that snivelin'," said Denton Offutt unfeelingly, and started aloft. "You kin stay, but mind you keep out of sight, and if you git us into trouble, I'll flay you alive and nail yore hide to the barn door! And keep away from that there jug!" he added. "Mind!" In outraged dignity he sat down in the shade made by the sail; there he preserved an aloof and wounded dignity.

Abe grinned down at their passenger. "Don't mind him. He threatens that to everyone, even me, but he wouldn't harm a hoptoad. He just has to brag and threaten like that to do his system good, like sulphur and molasses in spring. Bad to take, but it does *him* good. What's your name? We ought to have something to call you by, since you're going along with us."

"Dey call me Caleb, suh," said the man, wiping his eyes on his sleeve.

"Mine's Abe. Caleb, you hungry?"

"Yes, suh," answered the man. "I ain't et since yestidday noon when I run off."

"Open that there tin safe," directed Abe, climbing on deck, "and help yourself to a piece of pone. Might be an extra piece of fried pork left, don't know for sure. There isn't any coffee, but I'll make us some for dinner."

Jack Johnston, at the steering oar, looked wide-eyed with distaste at Abe when he resumed his job at the hickory sweep. "You know what you're a-doin', Abe Lincoln?" Jack said reprovingly. "You're aidin' and abettin' a runaway slave, and yore paw won't like it, nary bit!"

"I don't like it, myself," protested Abe. "But what are we to do? We can't turn a human being off to be torn by bloodhounds and beaten till his skin is raw, like it is now. Would you have the stomach to turn the poor critter over for more of it? No, you wouldn't, Jack Johnston, and Mr. Offutt, you wouldn't, either, for all your talk. No, Caleb is going to ride along with us and we'll keep mum about him. And if we know what's good for us, we won't breathe a word of the whole business to any living soul after we get to where we're going, nor when we get home, either. Remember that, Jack, will you? Not a word to Paw or anybody!"

"I sure won't!" breathed Jack in disgust. "Scared Paw will thrash the daylights out'n you, ain't you, Abe? *Hmph!* But I won't tell, not me. I don't want no one callin' *me* a slave-runner or a nigger-stealer. 'Tain't nice, and I want no truck with it!"

Abe nodded. "Mr. Offutt," he called to the still outraged little man who maintained silence at the front of the boat, where he reclined in the shade with his hat over his face, "Mr. Offutt, you heard what we said?" There was a grunt under the hat. "*We* want to keep this business a secret. Will *you?*"

Denton Offutt snorted and the hat fell off his face. He sat up. "By Tophet, Abe Lincoln!" he cried, his face red. "I never wanted to have *anythin'* to do with that feller in the *first* place, and I don't aim to ruin my reputation by ever *admittin'* that I did!" He replaced his hat over his face and lay down again with his hands folded over his fat stomach and his head pillowed on a coil of rope. Jack still looked with a degree of distaste at Abe who, with a grim expression around his mouth, kept his hands on the steering oar and his eyes upon the river.

CHAPTER TWENTY

THE FLATBOAT was considerably neater after Caleb joined the party. He washed up the few dishes they used and kept the frying pan scrubbed out with sand so that today's fried pork wouldn't taste of yesterday's fried catfish, or vice versa. He aired the blankets and brushed off the top deck—at night, when no one would see that a Negro was riding an Illinois freight boat. He found other things to do—he mended a rip in Abe's pants, washed shirts, and, for want of a smoothing iron, Caleb filled a tin cup with hot coals and used it to press out the wrinkles. His unending gratitude was embarrassing to Abe, but he endured it because he had to. Besides, young Lincoln was too busy navigating the Mississippi's curves to think much about the problems of a runaway slave.

Nearing Memphis, Abe called out, as they approached a group of islands, "Now we've got to watch out for Paddy's Hen and Chickens! Help me steer, Jack! We must bear left of the Old Hen—that's what they call the biggest island—careful of that sand bar—and two of her brood. Then we go to the right of the other. That way we stay in deep water. I hope the channel hasn't changed since three years ago!"

It hadn't. And eighty feet above the river, on the Fourth

Chickasaw Bluff, stood young Memphis with a hundred white ibises circling in the blinding, hot sunshine, a smell of molasses in the air, and bales of cotton on the wharves.

Abe pulled in and tied up the boat at the water front.

"They say DeSoto stood on that bluff, right up there, maybe," commented Abe, looking dreamily up at the city on the hill. "And he planned how he—"

"Injuns!" squawked Denton Offutt, interrupting him. "Speakin' of Injuns—by the Lord Harry, *look!*"

Abe hadn't been speaking of Indians, but he and Jack looked, and they could hardly credit what they were seeing as their eyes focused on real Indians there in Memphis, Tennessee. Indians along the water front, Indians along the street going into town, Indians seemed to be everywhere. The three voyagers could see hundreds of rangy horses, Indians moving among them, cookfires spiraling smoke into the circling flock of ibises. Indian children played along the shore.

Abe leaned over the bow of the boat and hailed a bearded riverman who hove into view just then. "Hey, there," Abe called, "what're all those Injuns doing here?"

"Oh, them," grunted the man sourly. "You must be greenhorns not to know. Them're Creeks and Choctaws and Chickasaws, and a bad bunch they be, I tell ye! Breakin' in and stealin' everythin' that ain't nailed down. Be glad when they finally clears out!"

"But why are they *here?*" Abe exclaimed.

"They're a-goin' west, thanks be," the man said fervently. "Gov'ment's payin' 'em to go west, to git out and leave Tennessee to decent folk. They been gatherin' in here fer weeks and it's about time they was loaded on boats and taken acrost so they kin start headin' west where they belongs. The Choctaws

HE NOSED THE FLATBOAT TOWARD THE SHORE AND SHE SETTLED INTO A
BERTH ON THE CROWDED, BUSTLING ST. LOUIS WATER FRONT

—DID NOT MEAN TO LET THE BOAT DRIFT . . . NOT ON OLE MISSISSIPP
WHICH CHANGED ITS MIND . . . FROM DAY TO DAY

and Creeks, they're pore; you kin tell one of them as fur off's you kin smell him, dressed porely and hang-dog lookin'. But the Chickasaws, they're rich as hog fat and *they* won't take sass from any white man *or* Injun. Most of the trouble we've had's come from them blamed Chickasaws. Mind you don't git in their way if you go into town. They'd as soon stick a knife in yore ribs as look at ye!" And the man spat a stream of tobacco juice into the Mississippi and stumped on his way.

In some perplexity, Abe and Jack and Denton Offutt looked at each other. They'd had in mind a day's holiday in Memphis.

"Oh, well, who are we to let an Injun spoil our fun?" said Denton Offutt bravely. "I tell you what we'll do. I'll stay here with Caleb on the boat and see nothin's taken, while you, Abe and Jack, go take your turn at seein' the town. Then when you've seen enough—and don't stay too long—you come back and stand guard while I go out for a little refreshment."

"Think you can manage, Mr. Offutt?" Abe asked, full of doubts as to what Mr. Offutt, even with Caleb's help, would do if a party of Indians tried to break in and steal the cargo.

"Oh, sure, sure, get along with you!" And Denton Offutt stretched himself out on the cabin roof. "Caleb'll call me if anybody tries to come up here. Doubt if they would in broad daylight."

Preparing for their first visit to a sizable town, Jack and Abe scrubbed up and shaved. Jack shined his boots and slicked his hair, and wore a fresh white shirt with ruffled cuffs, with his best coat and pants. Abe had nothing so fine, but at least he was clean, he consoled himself, and Caleb had put a smooth finish to his best shirt.

As Abe and Jack walked up the river street to the top of the red-earth hill which was the Fourth Chickasaw Bluff, they met Indians on every hand. Few looked happy. In most faces was reflected the grim acceptance of the fact that they now were an exiled people, leaving their ancestral lands forever. There were grim old chiefs heavily decorated with silver ornaments, chintz turbans, and buckskins; fat squaws and lean squaws dressed in long tunics with scalping knives as ornaments in their belts; raw-boned Indian horses loaded as high as possible with goods which the Indians were buying to take west into exile with them. They seemed to fear that out in the new Indian lands to which they had been banished, there wouldn't be much to buy. They were spending most of their government money in Memphis, to the great delight and profit of the Indian traders who were making the most of the chance to unload their wares.

Abe and Jack walked about for several hours. They did not enjoy themselves as much as they had expected. The day was hot and humid, more like midsummer than spring. Their shirts soon were wet with perspiration and they fanned themselves with their hats. Jack removed his good coat and carried it carefully over his arm, but he kept a firm grip on it so that no passing Indian could snatch it from him.

The two from Illinois were shouldered by Choctaws and Creeks, dressed almost in rags and very dirty; the riverman was right, you could smell them before you saw them. Abe and Jack were elbowed rudely by the glittering Chickasaws, especially at Isaac Rawling's trading post where the two paused to watch what was going on. Plenty was. Indian women were shrilly bargaining for tinware and gaudy pink china, glass beads and red ribbons, rock candy and needles and thread. The air was hot and close; it smelled too strongly of unwashed Indian. Jack's fastidious nose was offended and Abe agreed that it was pretty bad, so they returned to the street.

Here they were snapped at by skinny Indian dogs which yapped persistently and irritatingly at their heels and took a nip at their calves whenever the chance presented itself. Jack kicked out at one of the critters and sent it rolling and yelping in the dust. The boy's pale blue eyes looked up to meet the dark scowl of a six-foot Chickasaw in a red and blue turban who arrogantly crowded him off into the street where he fell flat on his face in the dirt. Abe yanked him to his feet and he came up with fists flailing.

"Let me at him!" Jack screamed. "I'll tear him apart, that—that—dirty—"

"*Sssssh!*" Abe hissed. "Quit it. Don't get in trouble with these Injuns. Come on, let's go!" Brushing furiously at his dusty clothes and raging at a rip in his best shirt, Jack stumbled away with Abe.

They had had enough. The place smelled. The Indians were in a bad mood. The dogs were more than anyone could bear. So Abe and Jack went back to the boat and Denton Offutt took his turn at seeing Memphis, but after a brief round at the nearest saloon, he, too, came back in disgust to the boat. The Indians were too much for Denton Offutt. One of them had spat all over his clean shirt front. Caleb was given the shirt to wash, and Offutt sulked for the rest of the day.

In addition, the news which Abe had to tell the little man when he came back to the boat didn't soothe his disposition.

"Mr. Offutt," Abe began, "I think we ought to leave pretty quick. While you were gone, I heard a couple of rivermen talking over on the wharf. Seems that flatboats are being searched for a runaway Negro. Don't know if it's Caleb they mean, but it wouldn't help any if they found him here with us. . . ."

Denton Offutt interrupted. "Well, I should say it wouldn't,

Abe Lincoln! I knew that there feller would bring us trouble.
You git him off right now afore they find him with us!"

"You know we can't do that, Mr. Offutt," Abe went on patiently. "Now, listen. I've got a plan that might work. When it's
getting near evening, we can cruise down along the shore below
Memphis and tie up there for the night. Then early in the morning Caleb can leave and nobody will be the wiser. Caleb," he
said, turning to the Negro, who was listening from the hatch,
"think you can make out, once you're on shore down there?"

"Yes, oh yes, suh, Mistah Abe," Caleb assured him, his face
beaming. "I'll keep me off the main roads till I gits me to Nashville. I got to find Celine and little Cal—'tain't right they should
separate us. We was married decent by a white preacher, Mistah
Abe, and he say over us—'What God hath jined together, let
no man put asunder.' And that's jist what they done. It ain't
right."

"What you goin' to do once you find 'em?" asked Denton
Offutt doubtfully. "They'll ketch you shore as fate."

"I don't know yet, suh," said Caleb, suddenly looking un-
certain. "I only know I got to find 'em."

So the flatboat slid unobtrusively away from the wharves
where other flats were tied up for the night, and when the city
was behind and only willow-grown banks lay to the left, Abe
steered toward shore. They would run a risk of attack by river
bandits by not tying up with a group of flatboats, but Caleb
would run less danger of being picked up.

Very early the next morning, Caleb, with tears running down
his cheeks and profuse thanks to all of the crew, and with a
parcel of pone and pork to stay him, slipped off among the mists
of the river woods and disappeared.

"Well, I surely do wish him luck," said Abe sadly. "But I got my doubts about him making out very long, even when he finds his family. It's a shame how they treat Negroes down here. You heard what he said the preacher spoke over him—it just isn't right to treat people so, no matter what kind they are!"

"You ain't seen nothin' yet, boy," said Denton Offutt glumly. "Wait till you see'm sell slaves and break up families right afore yore eyes, and them cryin' and carryin' on fit to kill whilst they's bein' dragged apart. Or see 'em beat with whips till their backs is runnin' blood—not hard enough to stop 'em from workin', but hard enough to show 'em who's boss. I don't guess it's right, but who are we to tell slave owners what to do? They paid good money for them slaves. And lots of 'em are treated real good, I know that."

"Poor Caleb," said Abe mournfully, pushing off from shore. "I hope he makes it, I surely do."

"And remember, both of you fellers," added Denton Offutt. "Keep mum about this deal. Don't let anyone know we helped a runaway slave to escape. We'd sure get in plenty trouble if it got around!"

CHAPTER TWENTY ONE

THE THREE on the flatboat awoke one morning at their mooring on the Tennessee shore to find the sky lowering and dark, the river iron-gray and very still, with no wind ruffling the smooth motion of the southward flowing current. There was a brooding silence along the banks. In the willows a song sparrow caroled half-heartedly. Breakfast was over quickly and the voyagers were on their way down the misty river when the first cold spatter of raindrops struck Abe in the face. They sent Jack and Denton Offutt to cover. Abe stuck it out as long as he could, then steered, half-blinded by the downpour, to the shore where he threw a rope around a sycamore and cinched it tight.

When he went below he found that Jack and Mr. Offutt were in a high state of irritation at leaks which sent drips of cold water into the bedding, onto the barrels, and upon their own persons. With Abe's help they threw canvases over the barrels and put the bedding in as dry a spot as possible, and then rolled themselves in blankets to keep warm. Everything in the cabin seemed damp, however, and when Abe tried to make a cook-fire at noon, the smoke almost choked them speechless. The fire would not burn and the smoke would not go out of the vent.

They ate cold corn pone washed down with river water, and it was not a pleasant meal.

They were wondering if the downpour would ever stop when they heard a sound which was neither rain nor river. A child's voice somewhere out there was saying:

"My pappy say you-all should come up to the house and git dry. We got us a fire in yon'."

Abe poked his head out. He saw at once that the rain was slackening, and that they had company—a thin, clean-looking girl-child of about ten, with a small face in which the brown eyes seemed too big and dark, long black hair in two braids down her back, and a faded blue print dress which hung limply to her ankles.

"My pappy say you-all should come up to the house," she repeated patiently. "Y'all must be fair soaked."

Abe, Jack, and Mr. Offutt had had no idea they were near a house. So many miles of the river shore along here appeared uninhabited. It was strange to find people and houses and cordial invitations like this one.

Abe crawled out of the hatch, unfolded his long legs, and seemed to stand tall as a sycamore above the child, who turned her eyes trustingly up to him. On the muddy slope, half-hidden behind trees, there was indeed a lone log house with blue smoke curling invitingly from the clay chimney.

"Well," said Abe politely, "seeing that you invite us so cordial, ma'am, we're beholden to you and accept with pleasure. The boat ought to be safe enough. Lead the way, ma'am!" It was the first time they had left the flatboat entirely unattended —and it was the last time, too.

The three followed the girl up the trail and came to a door which opened before them. A shaggy man in nondescript homespun held out his hand to them.

"Welcome, gentlemen," he said in courtly tones which would have done credit to a Kentucky landholder. "Welcome to our humble home. Come in and make yourselves comfortable."

Speechless, they entered, stumbling a little over the doorstep, awkwardly sinking into the hickory chairs. Four liver-colored hounds flopped their tails cordially on the floor, and then, drawing long sighs of content, collapsed in blissful comfort again. The fire was hot; the room was full of pleasant warmth. The three visitors sat and steamed before the fire.

The little girl was busy with the coffeepot. Abe started conversation rolling in the stark silence which began to engulf the room.

"Coffee, sir," said Abe appraisingly, as the child poured the steaming dark brew into thin, pink-figured china cups, and the scent rose in the air. "You're mighty lucky to have it way off here in the wilderness."

"Not so, suh," said the shaggy man. "We are on the main highway of America. Trading boats come past heah; we buy what we will . . . or sometimes get it in other ways. Now, back in Kaintucky, coffee wasn't always so easy come by. We'd sometimes have to resort to other brews."

"Kentucky," said Abe thoughtfully, sipping the hot coffee. The little girl was busy frying ham. Hot corn pone was browning in the spider. A pot of greens was almost ready. Brown beans were bubbling in another pot. "Kentucky," Abe reminisced, "I was born there."

"*Hmmm,*" said the man, eyeing with respect the young giant from upriver. "I guess maybe we shouldn't have left that blessed country, you and I."

"Then, why—" Abe stopped his question in midair. After all,

it wasn't manners to question your host. If *he* was willing to talk, it was all right, but it wasn't fitting to ask him how or why.

"Why did I leave? Suh, *that* is quite a story. But the short of it is this: they ran me out for a little business with horses. My wife had died and left me with the little one who is my right-hand helper now. I had nothin', just the few effects which I saved from my house before they burned it that awful night.

"We became wanderers on the face of the earth, suh, without a place to lay our heads. At last we started west, hoping to make a new life for ourselves. We built this cabin, suh, and now—well, likely this is where we'll stay. I don't hanker to go back to Kaintucky; we ain't exactly welcome there. But in the wilderness, a man's past don't matter, except to his own conscience." The shaggy man glowered at the fire. The little girl dished up the dinner and they sat around the deal table to as tasty a meal as Abe Lincoln had ever eaten. He smiled at the child and she smiled shyly back, then hid her face.

"You surely are a good cook, ma'am," he said politely.

The shaggy man, meanwhile, had been turning his gaze toward the door. Over and over again Abe had noticed it, as if the man were expecting more guests. Their host said, making conversation while they ate:

"I knew a gentleman back there who was a credit to Kaintucky," and he looked keenly into Abe's lean face. "In a way you remind me of him. I was a youngster—came up the Wilderness Road a piece with him. We had trouble one night and in gettin' away from Injuns I slipped over a ledge near the Gap and broke my leg. Mr. Lincoln saved my life and I know he saved me the use of my leg. Down in Kaintucky, suh, did you ever hear of a Mr. Abraham Lincoln?" And while he waited for Abe's answer, once more his eyes went with impatience to the closed door.

Abe felt his mouth drop open like a bear trap. Grandpappy Lincoln again!

"*My* name's Abe Lincoln, sir," he said in a smothered voice, laying down his fork. "He was my grandfather. I never saw him, but I heard Paw tell about him." Abe felt dazed. This was getting to be too much for him . . . he was meeting Grandpappy in the most unexpected places lately, and this was the fair limit.

"Well, now, to think o' that!" the shaggy man exclaimed, peering more intently into Abe's face. "Yes, I can see the resemblance. It's there. Mr. Lincoln was a very brave man," he went on meditatively, looking into the fire and frowning. "It is an honor for you to be his grandson and an honor for me, suh, to entertain you. And I'm afraid this puts a trifle different face on the matter . . . it does indeed," he added apprehensively, more to himself than to Abe. "More coffee, Polly."

The little girl filled the cups again and Abe, peering into the shining brown-black liquid in his cup, thought he could see the shadow of the Wilderness Road and his brave ancestors looking reproachfully at him. He wished he could get away from his family; they were always pulling him back or reproaching him for his shiftlessness. Paw never wanted him to get much schooling, called it a piece of nonsense, but Sarah Lincoln was different; she wanted him to learn, did all she could to get books for him. Sarah Lincoln never could do much with Jack, but Abe was like her own hopes made into flesh and blood and entrusted to her care. She could sense the dreams he dreamed and the plans he planned, and even if they weren't always clear to her, she knew they must be good. Without his stepmother— he called her Mother, as if they were blood kin—Abe knew with a deep affection that he never could have bucked Paw's anger at books and learning.

His brief reverie was broken suddenly as the heavy door swung open and a large man, wet with rain, heavily bearded, a slouch hat pulled low on his forehead, came in silently and stood with his back against the wall. Another man, no less forbidding, came in, and another, until six ruffians were ranged along one side of the room.

They said nothing at all. No one in the whole room said anything to break the tense silence which quivered with danger. The ruffians' eyes moved from one to another of the guests at the table. The men carried guns protected by their coats from the rain, and now in the warm room they silently brought out their firearms. Abe let his eyes run apprehensively over the assortment of rough, inscrutable faces. . . . He saw Denton Offutt sink down into his chair and grow white with fear, saw Jack freeze with alarm. The little girl vanished into the bedroom and closed the door softly behind her. The shaggy man's face took on a new look of command. Abe, in the midst of his distrust at what would happen next, saw how their host seemed to take a deep breath as he got to his feet.

"Gentlemen," he said softly to the silent men ranged along the wall, "these are my friends. Any harm which comes to them or to their goods will be answerable to me. You may go. And," his voice suddenly grew sharp and stern, "and don't you touch that flatboat or anything on it!" Abe saw how the ruffians lost some of their stature. Their faces cracked; their grimness was partly merged with confusion.

"You mean to say," growled one of the men, "that we come out in all this rain and then can't have our fun? Playin' jokes, eh?"

"Enough, Jim," said the shaggy man sternly, his voice no

longer soft. "You wouldn't understand loyalty, perhaps, but it's loyalty I owe these men with their flatboat which we expected to take. But we can't do it this time, boys. This young man," and he turned to where Abe sat tense, ready to spring if he was jumped on by any of the men, "this young man is the grandson of the man who saved my life on the Wilderness Road. I could no more countenance an assault upon him and his crew and upon his boat than I would countenance the same upon my daughter. Do you understand? *Hands off!*"

"We understand," growled a tall man with a bristling black beard. "And we'll keep our hands off. But if you play somethin' like this again, Jesse Hamilton, we might not give in so easy. Come on, boys." The six men slouched out and quietly closed the door behind them. Too quietly.

Denton Offutt was too scared even to open his mouth. Jack felt paralyzed in his chair. Abe unlimbered himself and stood tall above the shaggy man.

"I thank you, sir," Abe said coldly, "for the coffee and for the dinner and the hospitality of your home—also our thanks to Grandpappy Lincoln who, it looks like, saved our lives and Mr. Offutt's cargo. Now, if you have no objections, I think we'd better get back to our flatboat. I must have been crazy to think of leaving it unprotected for so long on this forsaken shore . . . if it hasn't already been broken into and looted!"

Without a word, Denton Offutt tottered to his feet; Jack Johnston followed close at Abe's heels. The shaggy man said nothing as the three went out and closed the heavy door.

Darkness had fallen. The rain had stopped but there was a steady *drip-drip-drip* from the newly leafed trees. After a moment of blindness upon leaving the lighted cabin, the three located the muddy path to the river where the massive flatboat, darker than the darkness, lay in the water.

It was a short yet endless walk from the cabin to the boat. Abe could sense danger all about in the dim, wet, spring woods. Somewhere those six men lurked . . . they had gone somewhere, and it could have been just outside the cabin, and they could be all ready to leap upon the crew as they came out and shut the door.

Abe felt a prickling on the back of his neck. Denton Offutt, who was making soft sobbing sounds under his breath, and Jack, who still could say nothing, kept close to Abe's side. And they got safely to the river. The woods were quiet and so was the shore; almost too quiet for comfort, like the way the door closed after the six men, thought Abe. The big flatboat heaved gently up and down on the water and there was no sound inside.

If a catamount had grabbed him when he slid feet first down into the cabin of the flatboat, Abe would scarcely have been more surprised than he was when he found no one there. He could hardly believe that the shaggy man's cohorts had not lain in wait for the return of the boat's crew. But the cabin was empty of invaders. He struck a light and lit the lantern. The boxes and barrels seemed intact.

"It's all right down here," Abe called in a puzzled voice to Denton Offutt and Jack Johnston. "I can't understand it, but there's no one here."

"Gosh-a-mighty!" burst out Denton Offutt, once he had his feet on the cabin floor and the trapdoor was locked above him. "I never was so scared in my life, Abe Lincoln! What you mean by goin' off and leavin' my boat to thieves and murderers? Why, everythin' could have been stolen and we could-a been killed in that villain's house. They're all a den of thieves, that's what they are, lurin' folk up to that house, feedin' 'em whilst they're bein' robbed, and then finishin' off the job by leavin' their bloody corpses floatin' in the river! By time, Abe, if you take chances like that again with my cargo, I'll git me a new pilot!"

"Calm yourself, Mr. Offutt," said Abe in exasperation. "I'll admit I was wrong in leaving the boat like that. Somehow the little girl seemed honest and it was a lonely shore, far from anybody. Seemed safe, I vow it did, and I admit I was wrong. I'll also admit that it was Grandpappy Lincoln who very likely saved our lives *and* the cargo! I never would have thought it, but that's exactly what happened, you saw it yourself. If that fellow up in the cabin hadn't remembered about Grandpappy saving *his* life on the Wilderness Road—*zssst!*" And Abe gave a quick motion with his index finger across his throat. Jack shuddered and Denton Offutt sat down because his knees felt weak. He reached for the jug and poured a tin cup full of applejack for himself.

"Have some, Abe," he said feebly, "it'll steady your nerves."

"My nerves are all right," Abe replied impatiently. "No, don't give any to Jack; Mother wouldn't like it. Jack's all right, aren't you, boy? We're all all right. Now what shall we do—shall we stay here the rest of the night or take a chance on hitting snags if we float downstream to a safer place?"

The same thing was in Denton Offutt's mind.

"I don't want to stay here a minute longer'n I kin help!" he cried. "I'd ruther chance the snags than a knife in my ribs!" This expedition was turning into a rather more hazardous adventure than he had expected it to be when he had planned it in Springfield.

"Whatever you say, Mr. Offutt," said Abe doubtfully. "I sort of think I'd rather get away, too, while we can. Those bandits may change their minds when they get to thinking of what they missed!"

Quietly they raised the trapdoor, and with Jack behind him, Abe went up to untie the rope. They shoved off into the river.

Coasting downstream without a spark of light to guide them was a dangerous business. Abe, at the steering oar, strained his eyes in the darkness, wishing for a moon to put a little light on the river, while he listened with more than his ears for the faint sound of water surging around and past an uplifted snag, for the whispers which meant shore and not river, shallows, not depths.

Although to Abe it seemed half an eternity of time, they had drifted along for only about an hour, when, before he was aware of what was happening, there was a soft pushing sound of wood on sand, and the flatboat came to a sudden halt. He went forward on the deck to investigate.

He had run the flatboat aground on a sandspit! With an exclamation of disgust, he dropped his big hands to his sides.

"There never was a worse flatboat pilot on this whole blamed river!" he cried. "We're stuck and here we'll stay till morning. Anyway, there are enough miles between us and the bandits to be safe, so we might as well turn in and get some sleep."

Denton Offutt, down in the cabin, had long since been blissfully slumbering. Jack and Abe crawled into their blankets and even though Abe expected to brood over this newest calamity, he, too, was soon asleep.

When he awoke the next morning, he went out on deck before the others were stirring to see what could be done. He was startled to find that the flatboat no longer lay aground, but was floating in water deep enough to carry her sidewise around the sandspit; in fact, the spit was some rods to the north already. Evidently yesterday's rain had raised the river level enough to carry the flatboat off its imprisoning barrier.

Jubilant at this pleasant turn of events, Abe shouted to Jack, who came up on deck, rubbing his eyes and yawning.

"Help me get her turned into the current, boy," Abe explained. "The river rose in the night and we floated off the sandspit, but we're broadside again. Won't take much of a turn to get her around—give me a hand."

Together they persuaded the big freight carrier to point properly downstream. By the time Denton Offutt came up on deck he found that Abe had breakfast cooking over a fire in the sandbox and the spit was out of sight. Since he was unaware of that latest aggravation, Abe and Jack said nothing about it. Mr. Offutt became disturbed too easily over trifles.

Placidly, in the bright May morning, the trio floated on south.

CHAPTER TWENTY TWO

Downstream the Arkansas, born in the mountains two miles above sea level near Leadville, Colorado, emptied its western silt and glacier water into the Mississippi.

As the flatboat moved around Spanish Moss Bend, the Illinoisans on board saw great gray hanks of Spanish moss hanging from the trees. The day was misty, the moss was dark and ragged after the winter, and the scene was one of desolation.

"Blasted witches' hair!" muttered Denton Offutt, who was in a bad mood that day. "I hate the blamed stuff!"

"Does look untidy, doesn't it?" said Abe agreeably. He and Jack were more concerned with the eternal crookedness of the Mississippi than with the appearance of the landscape.

"Can't we *never* go in a straight line?" Jack complained. "I git dizzy swingin' around and around all them bends. If the river didn't twist so much, we could git there in half the time!"

But no, ole Mississipp' had to take Bunch's Bend, which was fourteen miles around, yet the ends of the horseshoe were separated by only half a mile of swampland. You could almost meet yourself coming back when you hit the narrows between curves.

The flatboat passed Vicksburg high upon its bluffs. The wilderness of Arkansas lay across on the western shore. The twisting river now turned westward, made three large horse-shoe bends, then in great swirls and eddies came back to the bluffs. Whirling and eddying, the craft went with the current to Grand Gulf.

The boat was trying to get away from him, Abe decided. He could feel her leaving his control, could feel the river taking over. No longer could he flatter himself that *he* was guiding that flatboat down the Mississippi. As if hypnotized by the river, she was waltzing in peculiar curves. She was caught on the currents and now went north and east and west and south to get to where she was going. It was only twenty-five miles in a straight line from Vicksburg to Grand Gulf, but sixty by the course of the river, which for a long distance had had no straight lines.

Once more the steering oar seemed to have no power. Once more Abe's arms seemed to have no more say-so with the boat than if they had been made of yarn.

Now the craft hit a wild and cantankerous current which swung her in great deliberate circles, and Abe was frantic lest they swamp. Heavy as she was, she seemed as much at the mercy of the river as if she had been a chip on an eddy.

But at last they got out of the currents of Grand Gulf. From there to New Orleans the river lay like a cottonmouth sunning itself on a log.

That night the warm, moisture-laden wind which had been blowing up from the Gulf of Mexico for several days was met by a cold breeze out of the north. As the cold air struck the warm air, it condensed in fog. By dusk it was forming whitely in the bottoms, was blowing like smoke across the steaming river.

The fog closed in so suddenly that Abe, who had turned the steering oar over to Jack that afternoon, was caught off guard.

Next thing he knew there was a deafening blare of sound and a wild clanging of bells—a steamboat, big as all creation, had loomed out of the mist and was almost on top of them.

Abe leaped to the oar and Jack held on, too, and they pushed with all their strength to swerve the flatboat in time, but the steamboat was too close. There was a grinding crash as it struck the smaller craft a glancing blow along the side.

The mast toppled. Abe and Jack stumbled to their knees on the deck. Down in the cabin they could hear barrels rolling about and boxes falling.

Men yelled. The steamboat, unhurt, went right on and was swallowed in the engulfing fog.

The flatboat did not sink. She recovered gracefully from the blow. The wash from the steamboat rocked her crazily and waves splashed on deck, but they soon subsided. His knees shaking, Abe steered blindly through the fog in the direction of the shore—he hoped it was in that direction, anyway—and was relieved when he saw willows standing dimly in the gloom. The boat pushed to a willow edge and Abe tied up to a tree. Denton Offutt came pallidly on deck and for once had nothing to say.

By the time the supper fire was burning smokily in the sand-box, the three were enclosed in an eerie world of white. They knew that the river was out there, could feel it lapping at the boat, but they couldn't see it. The fog blew past, cleared a little, closed in, was always on the move and was growing thicker as the hours dragged by.

The trio on the flatboat could hear sounds out there on the water—sounds of boats going past, boats whose crews rang bells and beat upon pans, hallooed and shouted, anything to make a noise to avoid a collision. Voices like disembodied spirits went by. The three heard another steamboat passing, blowing its foghorn—a melancholy, resonant sound—and ringing its bells clangingly as it moved north. But they saw only the dimmest shadow of a shape sliding by and then the bells and the foghorn sounded farther away until they were heard no more. For a while the backwash from the paddle wheel beat noisily at the shore, slapped at the flatboat until she rocked. Finally it subsided. Somewhere out in the fog the three heard a woman's sharp scream. Again and again it came, again and again, one sharp, agonized scream after another until those sounds, too, grew fainter in the distance.

The fog was oppressive. To feel so shut in, to see nothing, to be out in the open wilderness with the biggest river in America running past and a big sky somewhere overhead, yet to be blinded by thick, wet, white fog—it was a terrible feeling, like being lost in a bad dream. It weighed upon them. They turned in early, but Abe lay listening to sounds in the fog. He wondered about the woman who had screamed. He was glad he was not trying to navigate through the fog as some boats were attempting to do. He wondered where Caleb was, and if he was hungry or cold or hurt, and if he would find Celine and little Cal.

When Abe awoke the fog had vanished. The sun quickly burned away the last vestiges of mist in the bottoms. The sky was brilliant and hot and blue. Summer had come along the Mississippi.

CHAPTER TWENTY THREE

IT WAS A glorious bright day when Abe Lincoln tied up the flatboat at the Natchez water front, there along old Silver Street. Even then, Silver Street was beginning to slide into the Mississippi, for Natchez-under-the-Hill was constantly at the mercy of the hungry river. This water-front section was the business end of Natchez, a ramshackle, dangerous place, the hide-out and hangout of river pirates and shady characters who roamed the river from St. Louis to New Orleans. Many a murder went undetected along that water front. The river told no tales. Many an honest man lost everything he had when he risked gambling with some of the professionals who stopped on Silver Street for loot. The decent people of Natchez lived in a town of their own, high on the bluff; they left Natchez-under-the-Hill to its own shady devices. After a while, no man, and certainly no lady, from the upper town could consider himself secure without a bodyguard when he paid a visit to the lower town. And the rivermen who stopped there had to watch sharply to depart with what they had brought with them, including their lives.

It never was safe to leave the flatboat unattended—least of all at Silver Street—so Denton Offutt and Jack Johnston stayed while Abe went out to see the town. When he came back, the others would take their own turns, one at a time. Offutt was more interested in the lower town, anyway, than in the fine mansions under the moss-draped oaks on the hill.

After a diligent scrubbing, a shave, and a quick polish to his boots, and the forethought to put on his other shirt—a move for which he was thankful later on—Abe started out. As he went, he wondered dubiously if he would find cargo, boat, or owner when he got back. But he went off, anyway, up the steep hill.

There he found a different world from the rowdy, smelly, water-front town lapped by the muddy river. Abe took a leisurely stroll for himself to see old Natchez. He ranged the length of Main Street, from the bluff's edge to the place where the street ended and the jungle of moss-hung oak forest began, and all along the way he paused to look at the fine houses and lovely gardens.

At a spot near the eastern edge of town he paused longest to gaze at a great house with white pillars and stately red brick walls glimmering behind the oaks.

He marveled at its grandeur, as he had at that of most of the Natchez houses. Nowhere in the Illinois country had he seen such houses—nor delicate, beautiful ladies like the two who walked with lace parasols in the garden into which he gazed, ladies who seemed to have nothing to do but look beautiful and stroll among masses of pink azaleas in the early May sunshine. Abe was conscious of a figure in purple who sat motionless on the verandah. Transfixed, dreamy, he forgot about the time.

He leaned on the wrought-iron fence. His elbow between the pickets and his chin on his hand, he just gazed at the fine house and at the two elegant ladies and a child in the distant garden.

The contrast between this—this loveliness, this peace and sweet-ness and cleanness—and the log cabin housing thirteen people on the Illinois prairie last winter, was somehow bitter to think about, and yet it was very wonderful, too. To know that such beauty could be, that people could live like this, that living wasn't all log cabins and corn pone and homespun pants and sweat-stained shirts—that, at least, was something good to think about. He wished his stepmother could see this. She loved beauty and had tried so very hard to bring a little of it into the stark cabins in which they had lived.

"Pahd'n me, suh," said a velvet voice at Abe's elbow. "I beg yo' pahd'n, suh, but may I be of service to yo', suh?" Abe whirled to see an elderly Negro man, meticulously dressed in plum-colored livery, standing beside him.

"Why—why—no, thank you, kindly. I was just looking at things and admiring them."

"Thank yo', suh, it *is* a sightly place," the old man said proudly. "Mah mist'is she say I should bring yo' in and offer yo' refreshment, suh, if yo' will be so kine." Turning, as if Abe's refusal was most unlikely, he led the way through the wrought-iron gate, and Abe, tall and lank and feeling as out of place as a Sangamon River sycamore log dropped into a camellia garden, clumped after him.

He saw nothing more of the ladies and the child, though the figure in purple still sat on the verandah. The elderly Negro led Abe around to the kitchen quarters. In the cool shadow of a brick portico there was a white bench.

"Pray to be seated, suh," the man said, and disappeared into the brick-floored kitchen depths. He was out again in a little while with a tall mug of cold milk and a square of gingercake—the first gingercake Abe had ever eaten. The taste of it on his tongue, followed by the creamy, cool milk, was one of the finest things he had ever known.

He ate, he drank, and he talked.

A group of Negroes gathered around to hear of his trip on the flatboat. They chuckled and they roared at some of the things he said, for one story led to another. The wrinkled face of the elderly houseman was wreathed in smiles of pure delight.

"That reminds me of a story I once heard," Abe went on, following a recital of his experience with the shaggy man up-river. "It seems there was a farmer that had been losing a lot of his fattest hens, night after night, because some varmint was getting into the henhouse and helping itself. So one night he set a trap, and next morning, what should he find in it but a skunk, smelling high-and-mighty of pure skunk perfume!" The Negroes grinned and hung on his words.

"Well, the man didn't know how he was going to get that varmint out of the trap and dispose of it without having more of the same sprayed all over himself. While he was standing there, the skunk spoke up:

" 'O, sir,' said the skunk—and Abe's voice squeaked in a falsetto, 'I pray you, don't kill me. I am not a skunk. I am your best friend, for I have come into your henhouse night after night to protect your hens from danger. Yet somehow they have vanished, but it is not my fault. I am your friend, sir.'

"The man looked hard at the animal. Yes, it was a skunk, all right; even with his eyes closed he could have told that. 'Well,' the man said, 'you look like a skunk and you act like a skunk, and my golly, you sure do *smell* like a skunk. So I say that's what you are!' And with that he blasted away and shot the skunk where it stood in the trap. Ruined the trap, too, and killed half the hens with the charge of buckshot!" And Abe grinned as his hearers broke into a burst of delighted laughter.

A little bell tinkled sweetly somewhere in the depths of the cool, dark house, and the old man made a quick and silent exit.

He came back, smiling all over his pleasant, gentle face.

"Mah mist'is, she say you should come with me, suh. She wishes to have a word with yo'. This way, suh."

Abe, numbed by the invitation, stumbled after his guide.

They went down a long, polished hall and through a room with a velvet rug. Abe tried to step lightly so that his rawhide boots wouldn't harm it. Only once before, on that other trip south, had he walked on such a thing. When he lifted his eyes in awe to the rooms he passed through, he was amazed at what he saw.

That must be a melodeon, he thought, catching sight of a musical instrument with a keyboard grinning at him. And look at those candles in silver candlesticks—that clock on the mantel must be solid gold! Land! And did you ever see such a looking-glass! And those paintings of people on the walls staring down disapprovingly, though he thought all the young men seemed like amiable dudes and the young ladies were unbelievably beautiful and frail. The deep red curtains at the windows, the shining dark furniture—bet somebody put a lot of spit and polish into *that* shine! He was lost in a maze of his own thoughts when the old man, with a bow, led him out on the pillared verandah where two ladies sat. Their skirts were spread silkily about their feet. He caught sight of a blur of purple but could hardly lift his eyes from the floor.

Abe Lincoln heartily wished he could drop through that floor and find himself back on Silver Street. He felt as out of place as an ox in a parlor—he *was* an ox who'd already been in the parlor and nobody had thrown him out—not yet. He was in an agony of embarrassment, but he stood still and tried to mind his manners. He held his old hat in his hands. Finally he dared to lift his eyes to the two ladies.

The one in purple was old and thin and had skin like white wrinkled parchment. Her purple dress made her look even thinner and whiter—she had white hair, too, with a snowflaky-looking lace cap on it—and sharp blue eyes peering intently up at him. The younger lady was stout and pretty and wore pink. Abe guessed quickly that they must be mother and daughter. The daughter looked as if she couldn't see Abe. But the old lady suddenly smiled and held out her thin hand.

"Come here, young man," she chirped. Abe took a hesitant step forward.

"Oh, come closer, do, I won't bite you!" she cried impatiently. "No, Maria, you won't catch anything from him. Don't shrink away. I know you're mortified to be entertaining a riverman but I *will* do as I please, won't I, poor dear Maria?" And the old lady grinned maliciously at her discomfited daughter.

"*Won't I*, Maria?" she insisted.

"Yes, of course, Mama," the daughter murmured. "But *really*, Mama—!"

"But really, Maria. I fancied the young man when I saw him mooning at us from the fence. Tell me, young man, what were you doing, planning on stealing the silver or begging a meal? Eh?"

And in great enjoyment the old lady leaned forward and peered impudently up at Abe's clean, sunburned, thin, embarrassed face, and at the hair that never would stay down. She looked him over, from his wild hair to his clumping rawhide boots, but she looked longest at his earnest eyes.

"Well?" she said, waiting.

"No, ma'am, not either one," he said soberly. "I've never seen such pretty houses and gardens, and I just couldn't help staring. I beg your pardon, ma'am, if I was rude. I didn't mean to be."

"No, you weren't rude, young man. Even from here I could see that. You interest me, young man. I like your face. What's your name and where're you from?"

"My name's Abraham Lincoln, ma'am," he said, wondering if *she* had known Grandpappy Lincoln, too! She was about the right age, most likely. "I came from Illinois. I'm piloting a flatboat of pork and corn to New Orleans for a man. That's all I am, ma'am, a riverman."

He saw the daughter shudder delicately. She kept her nose buried in her lace handkerchief and her eyes on the azaleas.

"Come now, Maria, you needn't lay it on so thick. He doesn't smell; he's clean and he has manners. And if you'd look at his face, you'd see he has something good and strong back of those bones. He's not a common, no-good-and-never-will-be riverman!" She turned back to Abe.

"Listen to me, Mr. Abraham Lincoln. I like you. Some day when you are your own master and haven't a load of freight to deliver, you come back here and talk to me. I heard some of those tales you were telling the darkies this afternoon—I eavesdropped—and I don't mind saying I enjoyed it, especially the way you got that boat of yours off the dam. Come back some day and tell me about the prairies and the forests and the wild animals and the Indians. And likely I'll tell *you* a thing or two about 'em, too. I will *not* be still, Maria. I'm proud of my adventures in the wilderness. Come back, Mr. Lincoln, and amuse me."

He was dismissed and he didn't know what to do or say to make his getaway. He stammered and twisted his stained old hat that had been his father's.

"I thank you, ma'am. I do appreciate your kindness. And I thank you kindly for that gingercake. It was the tastiest cake I ever did eat, and the milk, too—"

And with the old Negro to open the gate for him—as if he wasn't strong enough to open it for himself!—Abe in relief was off down the walk and out on the street again. When he looked back, the stout lady had vanished, but a little figure in purple waved a white handkerchief at him. With his big hand he waved back.

Abe still felt dazed and he felt good inside, too. The old lady had talked to him as if he was her equal. The Declaration of Independence might have said that all men were *created* free and equal, but they didn't all stay that way for long, and he knew it. The old lady was quality and he was white trash, everybody knew that; it had been dinned into him long enough. But if he was, she hadn't let it make any difference. It didn't matter to her that he was ugly and skinny and poorly dressed and that his folks were shiftless cabin people. Things just didn't happen that way to people like him. But they had, and he still could see the kindly, quizzical twinkle in the old lady's blue eyes. She was doing it all to spite her uppity daughter, maybe. Maria surely was fit to be tied at how her mother was carrying on with a riverman—but that gingercake and milk did him good, anyway.

He had lost all track of time. There was a late look to the sun. He took off at a run down the street and wondered in a flurry what had happened to Jack Johnston and Denton Offutt on Silver Street. Mr. Offutt would be mad at how he'd been kept waiting, Abe thought. Land, his mind ran on, I'll bet they've scalped Mr. Offutt and thrown his carcass to the jaybirds, and tossed Jack in the river for good measure. He was panting as he ran down the hill.

He found Mr. Offutt and Jack Johnston impatiently wondering what had happened to him. However, they were so relieved to see him safe that they weren't as angry with him as they had a right to be.

"Where you been?" cried Jack. "Thought you'd been snatched by bandits off the Trace!" He scowled at his stepbrother. "I been hearin' tales of the Natchez Trace; man robbed and murdered in broad daylight down there, two-three days ago. No place to fool around. Where in tarnation you *been*, Abe Lincoln? You spent nigh on to all day roamin' around and here *I* got to stick! 'Tain't fair!"

"I'm sorry, boy," said Abe. "I was safe enough," he grinned, "eatin' milk and gingercake on a lady's back stoop! But I'm sorry I kept you both waiting. I didn't aim to stay so long." And he told the incredulous Denton Offutt and Jack Johnston of his adventure with the gingercake, the old lady, and the wonderful house. Not quite all of it; they wouldn't appreciate it all, and he'd rather keep to himself his conversation with the old lady.

"Cain't hardly believe it," said Denton Offutt, studying Abe's face to see if he was fooling. "All I ever heard tell of Natchez was that the folk here was mighty high-toned and wouldn't even spit on a riverman, let alone look at him. How come they to invite you in like that, I want to know?"

"They were mighty nice to me, that's all I know about it," said Abe, remembering the graciousness and the peace and the beauty, and the cool taste of milk and the spiciness of gingercake, and how the old lady's blue eyes had flirted up at him, impudent as a girl's.

Jack took his turn at seeing the town, but nobody invited *him* in for refreshment, he complained, and he didn't stay long.

Denton Offutt didn't bother about the upper town; too much of a climb up the hill, and besides he found a crony in a saloon on Silver Street, so he spent the rest of his day without moving from that spot.

Next morning the boat cast off early. The goal was not far away, it was getting on toward the middle of May—and still the river flowed south.

CHAPTER TWENTY FOUR

LIFE WAS growing busier on the river. It took a good deal of careful and constant navigation to avoid all the steamboats and flatboats and keelboats going past.

"Never saw so many boats in my life," muttered Jack. "Always under foot, day *and* night!" Although Jack enjoyed the excitement, he hated having to be constantly alert, perpetually on the job. He preferred fishing from the stern or planning ways to make money without having to work for it.

On either side of the potent brown water of the Mississippi lay fields of cotton all in blossom. Black vultures hovered over them on motionless wings, or came down to perch on fence posts, where the huge birds sunned the night's dampness out of their glossy feathers. Sugar cane like tall grass was waving green in the wind. Pink mallows bloomed in the cypress swamps along the river; silvery gray moss hung like delicate spider webs from every cypress and tupelo; herons waded on the swampy shores.

From river landings, avenues of oaks led to the big plantation houses, set about with slave quarters and sugar houses; growing fields stretched to the forest's edge. Over and over, this was the scene which was repeated at intervals along the river. From Baton Rouge to New Orleans, the plantations went past.

Just beyond Baton Rouge Abe remembered something.

"It was down along here somewhere," he said reflectively, leaning on the steering oar, then guiding the flatboat around a large keelboat loaded with four families going south. They all waved merrily at the Illinois boat. "Can't recollect just where," he went on, "but it was some place close. We had tied up at Madame Duchesne's plantation for the night—Allen and I—when we had some trouble. Worst trouble we ever had on the river, worse even than our little experience back there with the gentleman from Kentucky!"

"What happened?" asked Jack.

"Well, we were asleep in the cabin when we heard shuffling footsteps and whispering on deck."

"What did you do?" cried Denton Offutt, remembering his own paralyzing fear on that dark and rainy night when he expected an attack at any moment.

"We crept out, and I grabbed up a club and Allen got a pole, and we lit into them. There were seven Negroes, big burly fellows," went on Abe with relish, remembering. "They were likely going to rob us, maybe kill us—that happens hereabouts. Louisiana is a wild shore. But we knocked some of them overboard and the rest ran.

"We chased 'em off into the cane thickets till we lost track of them, before we went back to the boat," Abe continued. "We were afraid to make a light, for fear they'd see where we were. Allen was bleeding from a cut on the cheek, and I got a deep one over my eye—still got the scar, too, you can see it now. But we decided we'd better get away from shore and float

"MY PAPPY SAY YOU-ALL SHOULD COME UP TO THE HOUSE," THE GIRL
REPEATED PATIENTLY. "Y'ALL MUST BE FAIR SOAKED."

IT WAS A GLORIOUS BRIGHT DAY WHEN ABE LINCOLN TIED UP THE FLAT-
BOAT AT THE NATCHEZ WATER FRONT, ALONG SILVER STREET

down the middle of the river till daylight, so they couldn't come
back, even if they wanted to, which I doubt if they did—we
gave 'em enough punishment to last a while."

"How come you to tie up here, anyway?" queried Jack.
"Didn't you stop with other boats, same as we mostly do now?"

"We most often did," explained Abe. "But Allen knew this
Madame Duchesne who lived up the levee on a fine big plantation. She was an old lady, dressed handsome; she was tall and
thin, and bossed her slaves as a lady should, firm but genteel
and kind. *She* never had any patience with beating slaves. Allen
wanted to stop and see her, so we did. She sent some of her slaves
to watch the boat while we had dinner with her—I remember
it was baked ham and chicken and sweet potatoes and pecan
pie. I can remember that yet!" Abe's deep-set eyes looked off
across the reaches of the brown river to a group of live oaks
on the levee and to a plantation beyond. "Over there it is." He
pointed suddenly. "I see it! Wonder how the old lady is now.
I've always hated running off like we did without telling her
good-bye, but it was safer to get away when we did. Think
we could stop, Mr. Offutt?"

Mr. Offutt said no. He wanted to get to New Orleans before
his pork began to spoil in the heat. And he didn't relish the
notion of an attack. He had had enough such frights for this
trip.

"Let's stick to the middle of the river," he said firmly, eying
the wild, grim, dark tangles of jungle closing in downstream.
"Gosh-a-mighty, is that an *alligator?*" he shrieked, as a long,
muddy shape slid from the shore into a bayou opening from
the river.

"Oh, you'll see lots of 'gators now," said Abe casually. "And

cottonmouths, too," he added, remembering certain somno-
lent, darkish, slumbering shapes draped on wet logs, shapes
whose white-lined mouths opened wide as a cotton blossom when
the creatures were provoked or alarmed.

Around the big bend lay New Orleans.

CHAPTER TWENTY FIVE

At the tremendous water front of New Orleans the flat-boats were lined up for almost a mile. A forest of masts stood up from ships out of far ports. There was the smell of the coffee boats; the perfume of spice ships from the Indies. There was the hubbub of men toting barrels and bales, men shouting, ordering, trundling goods about, with over all the lively noise of steam-boats letting off steam. It was a wonderful, exhilarating place and Abe's heart expanded with the joy of being back again, a part of all the activity and excitement of the Queen City of the Mississippi.

The water front was so crowded that Denton Offutt's flat-boat had to edge its way downstream nearly a mile on the *batture* before Abe could find an empty stall and nose her in.

Denton Offutt at once became the man of business. He brushed his best coat with care and buffed his hat on his sleeve, shined his boots with a piece of bacon rind, and bustled off. He paid the wharfage fee and the levee duties before he did anything else. Next he found a broker and sold his barrels and boxes of produce—evidently at a good profit because he looked pleased with himself when he came back to the boat and paid Abe and Jack their wages. He had sold everything, including the flatboat herself. Abe knew he was going to do it; nevertheless he hated to see her go. He had grown to love that big clumsy flat-boat built of Sangamon River timber.

There was a ready market for seasoned lumber like this. The craft had been a self-carrying lumber barge all the way from the Sangamon Country. No flatboat ever went back upstream—that uphill river which only steam had finally conquered—so now it was good-bye forever to the boat which had taken them safely out of the Sangamon and over the dam at New Salem, had carried them down the Illinois and through the traffic and contortions of the Mississippi—three rivers south. In spite of John Hanks's bad-luck screech owl on the shanty roof, the flat-boat had reached her goal. It was a shame to rip apart that good craft; her seams were tight, her pegs—Billy Masters' pegs—still firm. Abe felt that selling the boat was like selling part of himself, but he didn't express his feelings to Jack or Mr. Offutt. They would only have laughed.

The three from Illinois were going to stay and really see the place. A month in New Orleans! It was everything that San-gamo Town and Springfield and New Salem were not and never could be. It was a city of magic and a city of mystery. It could be as foreign in the French Quarter as France and Spain, as American as the cross-section of humanity that crowded the water front. New Orleans could be as exotic as palm trees in a courtyard, or as commonplace as Illinois oak planks steam-ing under a summer sun.

Every year, thousands of crewmen of flatboat, steamboat, and keelboat stayed on to see New Orleans and take part in—and contribute to—some of its rambunctious goings-on. And because so many rivermen came from Kentucky, the New Orleanians for a long time called them all "Kaintucks" and hated and feared them with a most cordial and enduring passion.

Summer heat moved stickily over the city. The white blossoms of magnolia trees perfumed the walled gardens where mockingbirds sang madly all night long when the moon was full. Abe and the other "Kaintucks" roamed the strange old city— even in 1831 New Orleans was old.

This was the city Abe Lincoln saw . . . the New Orleans which was begun in 1718 in the big crescent of the Mississippi . . . the New Orleans which for many years was pure French, a city built in a swamp, hewn out of the cypresses and cane and Spanish moss, where alligators moved grudgingly out of the way.

The first houses were square huts set in the mud, and when fine ladies and gentlemen from Paris came here to live in what had been pictured as a beautiful French city in *L'Amerique*, their elegant clothes became considerably bedraggled. Many of the French died because of the low-country ills which attacked them; many went back to France where they could count on paved streets and decent houses, and no Indians on the doorstep. But others stayed. Grimly they stuck it out. They drained the swamps; they threw up levees; they built better houses. However, the streets were still full of mud, and there were still Indians and alligators.

One spring day in 1788, a fire began in one of the frame houses, and before the flames were put out most of the old French homes were gone. Before it was rebuilt, New Orleans came under Spanish rule, and the city thereupon was rebuilt according to Spanish ideas of architecture. Only a few of the original French houses which escaped the fire remained to show what the old New Orleans had been like. The Spanish imported wrought-iron balconies from Spain, built brick and stucco dwellings rising straight up from the sidewalks but with beautiful enclosed gardens and courtyards behind each house.

In rebuilding the city, the wealthy Don Andres Almonester y Roxas contributed the Cabildo, or government house, the hospital, St. Louis Cathedral, and the Capuchin monastery, and lived to view with pride the results of his generosity, ranged around the grassy park called the Place d'Armes, not far from the water front.

And New Orleans became a city of Creoles, a mingling of French and Spanish with their own manners and customs and language, which were neither French nor Spanish, nor were they American, but a mingling of all three which could be found only in New Orleans.

Although in 1800 the city passed by treaty back to France, it was no longer the French city which it once had been, but was still and forever Creole. And then in 1803 Napoleon casually sold New Orleans to President Monroe. With it went 885,000 miles of land and water northward. For fifteen million dollars, the United States acquired New Orleans, and along with it the great Louisiana Territory, which included the Mississippi River.

New Orleanians went into mourning. Their beloved Emperor had betrayed them—Louisiana disposed of at a mere four cents an acre—people sold like slaves to America, which to the Creoles was a land of barbarians! To that country of which the Creoles had never felt themselves really a part. It was the land of the rough "Kaintucks" who came downriver on crude flatboats every spring and swaggered and cursed and fought and drank, and by their brawls and bloodshed caused endless trouble to the natives of New Orleans. When, like a wounded bird, the French flag fluttered down and the Stars and Stripes brazenly went up in the Place d'Armes, the people wept behind their shuttered windows.

Then came the War of 1812. Not until the greatest battle on American soil took place in 1815, on the Plains of Chalmette, near New Orleans, were Americans accepted in Louisiana. Americans were heroes; they had beaten the British. And with so many heroes about, the Creoles began to accept them as friends and compatriots. The city grew used to being American and rather liked it. The people named their Place d'Armes Jackson Square and some years later they erected a statue of the American hero, Andrew Jackson, in the middle of it.

CHAPTER TWENTY SIX

A MONTH IN the dangerous old city which was New Orleans in 1831 could hardly be dull. To Abe and Jack, sallying out together to explore the city, it was a month of bright days highlighted by danger, mystery, romance. For the most part, Denton Offutt went his own way and they seldom saw him except when Jack went to Offutt's haunts at the water-front hangout of rivermen, called The Swamp, and Abe followed his stepbrother there to persuade him to leave.

Abe and Jack had rented a cheap room in Gallatin Street. They chose it because it was cheap, for they hadn't very much money to spend on a month's lodging. Gallatin Street was in a tough district—a short street, rowdy, bawdy, perilous. It was close to the French Quarter and to the water front, but although it was so conveniently located, Abe more than once wondered if it might not have been wiser, though more costly, to have taken a room in a more decent part of the city.

Still, their frowsy landlady, gaunt Madame Ambrose, did not see much of her Illinois tenants, who every morning left their dirty, dark, rat-infested room up under the eaves of her house on Gallatin Street and went out to explore the city. Sometimes they worked for a day or two at the docks to add to their supply of cash, but the remainder of their time was spent in roaming the crooked, narrow streets of the old city, or sight-seeing elsewhere.

To a young fellow like Abe Lincoln, whose formal education amounted to less than a year, a month in a city like New Orleans, a month properly applied and attacked by a curious and receptive mind, was better than a year in college. He would have a lot to tell his sympathetic stepmother when he got back home. And he really should buy her a present. She would be so proud if he brought her something all the way from New Orleans. Sarah Lincoln would enjoy hearing of this whole adventure, from first to last; yet he doubted if even she would comprehend some of the things which happened—the fortuneteller, the old Cala-bozo, the time he had to haul Jack out of The Swamp, or the mysterious lady who threw Abe a rose.

He and Jack often went to the French Market for coffee and fried cakes in the morning, the Market where foods were sold which neither Abe nor Jack had ever seen before. The people at the Market—Cajuns from across the river, French and Italians from New Orleans, Choctaws from the swamps, Negresses frying chickens and shrimps, nuns buying fruits for the convent kitchen, burly black Negroes trundling barrows full of cabbages —were even more interesting.

One day a mulatto fortuneteller—who was seated, as usual, on a red cushion on the damp floor of the French Market—reached up a long thin hand and plucked at Jack's trouser leg. Startled, he looked down.

"Listen, m'sieu, and I tell your fortune," she whispered in a soft, husky voice. "Marie-Babette knows all and nevair lies—listen to Marie-Babette!"

"Wait a minute, Abe," called Jack to his companion, who had

walked on, not noticing the delay. "Let's see what she has to say." Jack, with his easily flattered vanity, was anxious to hear his fortune. He was sure it would be a good one.

Good-humoredly, Abe waited; he put his hands in his pockets and leaned casually against a stucco pillar.

"Silver, m'sieu, silver for Marie-Babette, before she speaks—" Jack fished out a coin and dropped it into the pale, coffee-colored palm.

"Ah, *merci, merci beaucoup*," the woman murmured in that strangely compelling voice. Half-shutting her eyes, she said, "Show me your hand, and I tell your fortune."

Jack let her hold his neat hand in her cold fingers.

"I see great wealth for m'sieu," she whispered. "Ah, great wealth, gold—gold—gold! And a fair one for his bride—ah, and a long journey that m'sieu must beware of. And m'sieu, beware of thieves!"

Jack jerked away his hand as if he had burned it, and thrust it reassuringly into his pocket where he kept his money. No thieves would take *his* wealth if he could help it!

The woman plucked at Abe's bony leg. "Your hand, m'sieu, and Marie-Babette tells your fortune. A piece of silver for Marie-Babette—"

"Go on, give her some," urged Jack. "See what she says about you!" Jack, though alarmed at the prophecy of theft, was still considerably puffed up about his impending wealth.

Abe was curious enough to part with a coin. Over his big hand, the pale brown woman bent her head with its crisp white *tignon* and gold earrings.

As she looked at his long, hard fingers, his palm calloused and creased with hard work, her face grew still and withdrawn.

"M'sieu, you must beware," she said at last. He could hardly hear her low voice. "I see a dark lady who will cause you joy and pain. I see blood—blood—m'sieu must beware. I see no wealth for m'sieu, alas, but I—I see so strange a thing—" She paused and looked up at Abe's thin, tanned face with its thoughtful eyes and big, quizzical mouth. "M'sieu—you will not believe me, but you will live forever!"

Abe laughed. Jack slapped his leg and guffawed. "That's a good one—by golly, Abe, that beats mine all hollow! Old etarn'l Abe, goin' to live forever!" And Jack could hardly straighten up for laughing.

"Thanks, ma'am," Abe said politely to the woman as they walked away together, still laughing. The fortuneteller sat watching them quietly as they went.

There was another day when Abe and Jack walked past the old Spanish Calabozo or jail. It was a dark, gray, forbidding building with grim windows. There Abe and Jack halted suddenly. Agonized cries and groans came from a rusty grating beside the wooden sidewalk.

Abe felt himself grow a little pale. Jack gripped his arm.

"What is it?" he whispered.

"Someone moaning and carrying on down there," Abe said in a stifled voice, more to himself than to his stepbrother. "And a whip lash—must be a whip— Listen to it, Jack. I can't *stand* listening to it—let's leave!" Although Jack protested that he wanted to stay and find out if they could see what was going on, he followed Abe's long strides away from the Calabozo. There, in the cellar of the old building, one could send his erring slaves for a suitable whipping, without the bother of doing it at home, and for the payment of only a trifling sum! More than once after that, Abe, awakening from a bad dream, shuddered again at the memory of those wrenching, awful cries. He had never heard a man being beaten before, and the thud of the lash on living flesh was too vile to think about. It haunted him for days.

During his waking hours, however, Abe was more concerned about Jack than about his personal memories. Jack had fallen in love with cockfights and sought them out. He had discovered that fights regularly took place at The Swamp, the rowdy, waterfront rendezvous of the rivermen. Abe worried about him. He knew that The Swamp was no place for anyone who valued his safety or his money, and a young fellow like Jack would be at the mercy of the older, tougher men who frequented the place. But Jack was fascinated by it. He boasted that he had talked to some real pirates, some of the men from Barataria Bay who had sailed and fought with Jean Lafitte. But most of all he was fascinated with the exciting cockfights, where betting went on furiously and he found he could make money fast.

"It's a whole lot easier than workin' all day totin' bales and barrels on the docks," Jack announced, when Abe tried to keep him away. "Anyway, it's fun and them fellers been real nice to me. Maybe I'll get rich, like the fortuneteller said, and I ain't goin' to pass up a chance like that!"

But one evening when the river mists thickened along the water front and made a pale glow around the few street lanterns illuminating the crossings, Jack failed to return. After pacing about for several hours, Abe finally started out to hunt for his missing stepbrother.

First he went to the cockpit back of the Cathedral where Jack sometimes lingered; no one had seen the boy. Abe searched among the low dives along the water front; Jack was not there. Next Abe investigated The Swamp. He usually avoided this place. Not only was it dangerous, but he hated the cruelty of cockfights.

As he pushed open the heavy door of The Swamp, wild yells greeted him. In the smoky, odorous, low-ceilinged room, murkier than ever with the river mists which had seeped in, he saw the men crowded around something at one end of the room. He couldn't see Jack, nor could he see what the others were looking at. Abe climbed on a table top and peered over the men's heads.

It was a cockfight; he might have known. The winning fowl, a green-hackled young rooster with one eye missing, had just feinted and with his wicked spurs had ripped open the breast of his opponent. Blood spurted and the dying cock flopped and croaked and struggled while the men cheered and laughed. In the front row Abe saw Jack's pale hair. Jack was yelling and cheering with the rest.

It was over. Jack turned and saw Abe as he was getting down from the table. "Hey, boy—look at me!" cried Jack gaily and incautiously. "I'm rich! The lady was right—I won eight times running, and I'm rich!"

His boasting was his downfall. Before he reached Abe, two silent dark ruffians reached out and knocked him down. The boy kicked with both feet and screamed, but one calmly took all his money and vanished in the crowd, while the other held him down. Before Abe could get to him, the boy was rolling and tumbling with his assailant. Abe climbed over tables and knocked over chairs, then with flailing fists hurled Jack's enemy into the crowd. Suddenly, as so often happened in that impartial spot where brutality met brutality and robbery met robbery, the men in The Swamp were taking sides in a general melee. Bottles flew, glass broke, chairs crashed, men cursed, women screamed, a pistol went off.

In the turmoil, Abe yanked Jack to his feet, half-carried the boy to the door and got him out into the misty darkness. Jack was sobbing. He held his hand to his nose, which was bleeding profusely down his shirt front, while he fumbled for his handkerchief.

"They t-took all my money!" he wept. "I got to go back and get it back from them—them pirates! I was rich—I won a hundred dollars, Abe, and now I—I ain't got any l-left!"

"Never mind that," said Abe sternly. "You're lucky to be alive. And if I catch you in that place again, money or no money —Jack, you realize those cutthroats in there would kill you for less than that?"

Next morning when the two came down the littered, dusty stairs, their landlady, Madame Ambrose, moved from the door-step where she was sunning herself, to let them pass.

"Heh, heh," she cackled. "To think of seeing you this morning! When I learned that two men were killed in The Swamp last night, I thought—ah, that's my two fine Kaintucks. I was all ready to go and clear out your room and keep what I found, heh, heh, heh!" Jack smiled wanly. His nose still hurt. Abe did not smile.

Not all of their days were so grim, though. Most of them were full of discoveries, full of fun. One evening, long after the sun had set beyond the broad, smooth waters of the Mississippi and the aromas of the coffee boats, mingling with the smells of the open sewers, came more strongly on the evening breeze, Abe and Jack were heading briskly down Chartres Street when suddenly a door on a gallery was thrown open. Light, music, and laughter floated forth as a beautiful young girl in a lace mantilla danced out.

She looked quickly through the iron grillwork, saw Abe and Jack as they walked under one of the large oil lanterns which hung at street corners. Laughing over her shoulder at someone in the brightly lighted room and crying out something Abe couldn't understand, she flung a red rose over the railing, flung it straight at Abe and it landed on his stained old hat.

He plucked off the flower and stood holding it in his fingers. He stared up at the girl who, still laughing, waved her white hand and vanished into the room again. He stuck the rose in his shirt front and, not saying a word, went on. Jack, however, now and again cast a slanting glance up at his stepbrother, who was looking straight ahead. The oddest things were always happening to that Abe Lincoln.

It was very dark. A cannon let go a resounding boom.

"Nine o'clock," commented Abe, quickening his steps toward the dismal, ugly, brutal Gallatin Street. "That's the warning to soldiers, sailors, and Negroes to get off the streets. They enforce it, too. There isn't any law says *we've* got to get off, but we might as well. We had a long day and I'm tired, aren't you, boy?"

"Sure am," remarked Jack, still looking at the red rose.

CHAPTER TWENTY SEVEN

"MAYBE I'LL never get back to New Orleans," said Abe one morning. "And I want to go see the place where Andy Jackson fought the British. I've never seen a battlefield, and they say this was the biggest battle America ever fought. Want to come along, Jack?"

Jack Johnston yawned. The Louisiana climate was getting the better of him. Even in the more vigorous climate of Indiana, he never had much ambition. Now he liked nothing better than a chance to rest instead of tramping the streets with the insatiable Abe, who could walk the feet off a thousand-legger.

"Not me. It's miles out, ain't it? I'm goin' to stay here and rest. You like to wore me out walkin' out to that there Lake Pontchartrain yesterday."

Abe, from his six-feet-four of height, looked disapprovingly down at the supine form of his stepbrother, reclining on the dirty bed.

"I should think *anything*, even a long walk through the swamps, would be better'n lying in that filth!" But Jack, particular as he was about his clothes, wasn't disturbed by the state of his bed.

Abe went out North Rampart Street and headed southeast

into St. Bernard Parish. It was a pleasant walk. The sun was warm, the road was not muddy, and the gray moss hanging in the oaks looked light and pearly and fresh, with none of the dank somberness of some of the moss along the river. Cardinals whistled and flowers were in bloom. Abe whistled, too, as he strode along, and he knew a singularly happy and lighthearted feeling. He was alone and unencumbered with his less imaginative kinfolk. He had no obligations to anyone and a day to call his own. His long legs felt as if they wore winged boots, and his head was in the sunshine.

As he walked, he admired here and there the fine homes he passed, for St. Bernard was one of the earliest parishes to be settled around New Orleans. When he came to a house near the Mississippi he paused and asked a passing Negro boy to whom it belonged.

"Oh, dat belong to Mistah Macarty, suh," the boy replied politely. "Gin'rel Jackson, he done had he's headquawtah dah, endurin' de big battle, suh. De Gin'rel, he used to walk up and down dat gallery, dah, walkin' and walkin', up and down, up and down, figurin' out in he's haid just how he gwine to win de wah. And he done it, too!"

"Thanks, son," said Abe, glowing at what he was seeing and hearing, and he gave the boy a picayune for his trouble.

Abe felt he was getting close to his goal. The next Negro he saw, he inquired where the battlefield might be.

"You on it, suh. It war fit right heah wheah we standin', mighty nigh!" Abe felt a quiver run through him as he seemed to sense the strength in that blood-soaked earth and to hear the commands of Andy Jackson and the rumbling of the guns.

He could see a slight depression and humping up of earth along a row of hackberry trees. "Oh, dat Gin'rel Jackson's earthworks, suh," said the Negro, following his gaze.

Beyond the open space which was Ignace de Lino de Chalmette's sugar fields, where much of the battle was fought, cypress swamps extended to the river shore. In all that peaceful, sunny swamp and field and forest, sweet and undisturbed now on a day sixteen years later, there had taken place one of the most horrible battles of American history. Horrible because it was all so unnecessary, a battle which was fought after the war was formally ended.

When word arrived that the British fleet was coming, all New Orleans was in a turmoil and day and night the churches were crowded with praying women. Andrew Jackson was in command of American forces and got there with two thousand untrained men who had been gathered up from Tennessee and Kentucky, from Illinois and Missouri. There were Choctaws from the swamp country; even Jean Lafitte was there with his swaggering pirates from Barataria Bay.

Abe remembered reading about it somewhere—how General Pakenham, the fine British commander, all decked out in his pretty uniform, heavy with medals and gold braid, came with nine thousand picked men who had fought nobly under the Duke of Wellington and knew the art of warfare. But they hadn't known American warfare. And they didn't know the Louisiana kind, which was something very different. They landed near De la Ronde's and De Chalmette's lands, and there in the cottonmouth swamps they fought the greatest and grimmest battle in American history. The British knew nothing about how to fight in swamps where alligators and poisonous snakes lurked, or among the confounded entangling gray moss which cut off their view through the trees.

Abe, standing in the sunshine, knew how they must have felt

—desperate, trapped, confused—while the American back-woodsmen, who had been weaned on swamps and snakes and gunpowder, lit in and slaughtered them.

The Americans, anyway, were defending their homeland and that made all the difference. When the battle was over and the guns were still after those two bloody hours on a January day, General Pakenham himself lay bleeding to death under a tree, maybe that one over there, thought Abe.

Pakenham had lost, besides his own life, the lives of seven hundred men; fourteen hundred were wounded; five hundred were taken prisoner. And General Jackson—good old Andy who knew his swamps and his backwoodsmen—had lost only six men and had seven wounded. That was when the Creoles started loving all the Americans, even rivermen, even "Kain-tucks" like Abe and General Jackson.

But the thing that made Abe think soberly was the good, hot, living blood which had been wasted. For the Treaty of Ghent ending the war had been signed on Christmas Day, 1814, but the news was so slow in reaching Louisiana that it didn't arrive until three weeks later. By that time Andy Jackson had defended New Orleans and the British had lost an army.

Abe spent the rest of the day poking around the battlefield. On the old earthworks he turned up some lead bullets and put them in his pocket. He walked east along the road to Versailles plantation, where the De la Rondes still lived, and asked per-mission to explore the long avenue of arching oaks leading to the river landing in order to see more of the battle site.

A young Negro at the plantation house gave him a drink of cool water from the well, and the cook came out on the shadowy brick porch with a bowl of strawberries and thick cream for him to eat. People were always thinking Abe needed feeding.

"You been lookin' over de battlefield, is you, honey?" asked the cook. "Well, you is in de right place, yes suh! And if'n you-all will go to M'sieu de Villere's plantation, down past de La Coste house, suh, you'll find dat *pee*-can tree where-at dey buried de Gin'rel's heart."

"His h-heart?" stammered Abe. "You mean to say they buried his *heart* and not the rest of him?"

"Yes, suh, it's God's troof, suh. Dey see de po' Gin'rel bleedin' to def and dey laid him down gentle under de *pee*-can tree, and when he done die, dey took'n out he's heart and dey buried it 'neath dat tree. And de *pee*-cans is always been streaked with red, ever since, with Gin'rel Pakenham's blood."

Blood—somehow Abe felt there was too much of it hidden in this Louisiana country. The sense of nearness to the battle and to death was suddenly oppressing. Thanking the cook and her assistant, he started off toward New Orleans.

When he got back to the dirty, smelly, little room in Gallatin Street that night, it seemed even more dirty and smelly because of all that splendid sunshine and fresh air of the Louisiana bayou country, the glorious cypress swamps, and the story of the great battle.

He found Jack still lying on the bed. He had been sick and wished he was home. The New Orleans food, Jack moaned, didn't agree with him.

Abe crawled into the smelly bed and tried to sleep, but he kept thinking about the Battle of New Orleans and the blood-soaked Plains of Chalmette.

CHAPTER TWENTY EIGHT

Next day, when Jack was still laid up with indigestion, Abe again went out on his own. It was better than killing time in that dark little Gallatin Street room where the rats were as big as tomcats, almost, and the cockroaches disputed the right of way across the floor with you. Abe had just about decided to find a better place to live while they stayed in New Orleans.

He went creaking down the littered dark stairway and left Jack groaning on the sagging bed.

"I'll go get you a powder," Abe promised, "if I can find a druggist that can speak American."

He went out into the fresh air and walked away from the foul-smelling, murderous street.

He walked out into Esplanade where a Negro banana vendor pushing a rickety cart cried out his wares in a tongue Abe couldn't understand. An immaculate, tall, stately Negro woman with a basket balanced on her white *tignon* sailed past him crying "*Callas, callas, tout chaud!*" Abe Lincoln hadn't the slightest idea what was in the basket or what she said, and he hadn't enough nerve to up and ask her. It was a funny feeling to be in a city where folk didn't understand plain English, and who spoke a lingo which made no sense, especially the way they gabbled it. Made a fellow feel homesick and far from his own people.

He walked into a little shadowy side street and almost passed a single, narrow shop window set in the brick wall. It had a lot of queer things in small papers which were laid out as if they were for sale. There was blue powders and yellow powders, black powders and tiny tufts of rooster feathers tied in bunches with black thread. There was a saucer of queer dried things like nail parings, a bowl of what looked to him like dried bats, a hank of hair that was gray and stringy and dead-looking, a paper full of dried fish eyes, and a bottle of red stuff, thick and dark-looking, like blood. The place might have been a druggist's shop, but he had his doubts.

"Go 'way, w'ite man!—You, Kaintuck, *git* away fum dat window. Dat's voodoo stuff and you don' got no business hyar!" said a deep, surly, resonant voice. A very large and burly Negress, coal black and fierce and shiny, with hands on her broad hips, stood eying him from a dark doorway.

"Git, you-all!" She spat at him, and Abe got. He was pretty sure that Jack's stomach ache wouldn't have been relieved by anything in that window, whatever voodoo was.

He went out into Royal Street. He always enjoyed walking there. He loitered along, looking into shop windows and wondering what lay behind all the tightly closed windows, and thought again about the beautiful lady who had thrown the red rose at him. That was a funny thing, he mused, smiling to himself.

He had just passed a large, tightly-shut doorway when a smaller door, set in the larger one, opened quickly and a lithe young Negress stepped out. She hurried up to Abe and touched him imperiously on the arm.

"Please, suh, you are to come with me," she said.

Abe looked down at her pretty face with its finely modeled bones. He'd never seen her before. Nobody knew him in New Orleans, not a soul. He didn't know if this was a trick or not—he'd heard about such things, and there was that little girl who had invited them, sweet as honey, into the shaggy man's house which was a trap. But Abe wasn't rich enough to rob, and nobody'd want him for anything else, he reasoned. The girl's face looked honest, though determined to have her way. Abe decided to take a chance and see what was up.

"All right, ma'am," he said. "I'm with you."

The girl held open the little door. He had to duck his head to enter and she shut it behind him, bolted it from the inside, and dropped the chain across it.

They were in a damp, dark passageway, like a low tunnel. At the end of this was a doorway covered with an ornamental wrought-iron gate, beyond which lay a garden. The girl unlocked this gate and when they had gone through it she locked it after them. Two locked gates now lay between him and the street, Abe tallied, and he began to feel just a shade uneasy. But he was still curious enough to follow the girl. If anything happened, it was his own fault.

The walled garden was floored with damp, mossy flagstones. A stone fountain played sweetly with tinkling little splashes in the middle of the cool courtyard, and in the water swam shining red fish. A macaw with vivid blue and yellow feathers and a long tail perched on the side of the fountain and occupied itself by dropping pebbles, one by one, into the water. At sight of Abe Lincoln, the creature cocked its head and let out a shrill screech which went right through him, and then it flew on its remarkable wings to a banana tree. In a niche beneath and behind the drooping leaves of the banana tree he saw a small white

155

statue of the Virgin Mary.

"You will please to be seated, suh," the girl said, and showed him an iron chair beside a little table. He let his lanky length fold down uncomfortably into it and fiddled with his hat. He wondered what came next. The macaw screeched at him, and a little black monkey, ugly as an imp of Satan, came scuttering across the flagstones and ran up his leg and into his lap. In startled panic, he swept it off—he'd never seen a monkey before —and the little creature crouched on the flagstones and bared it teeth and grimaced and chattered at him. Then he heard quick footsteps and looked at a dark, arched doorway. A lady in black stood there, leaning on a gold-headed cane.

She paused a long moment and gazed at him.

"Well, Abe Lincoln, so it's really you. I told Delphine to bring you in. I was almost sure it was you, *cherie*—there aren't many young men so tall. But three years can change one as young as you, and perhaps my eyesight is not as good as it was then. How are you, Abe?"

Abe sprang to his feet and dropped his hat. The monkey darted in, snatched it up, and scuttled to the back of a chair where the creature sat turning the hat around and around in its skinny little black hands.

"M-Madame Duchesne!" Abe gasped, holding out his big hand. "*How are you*, ma'am?"

"Tolerable, Abe, tolerable. Where is Allen—I did not see him. Is he not with you, then—you dreadful Kaintucks from up North?" She laughed affectionately, a silvery, not unkind little laugh which proved she really was fond of "Kaintucks." She came to Abe and shook his hand, then seated herself beside the little table. Abe settled down again into his chair.

"Allen's not with me, ma'am. I've left Indiana for good. I'm from the Sangamon Country in Illinois now. My folks moved there last year. I got me a job piloting a flatboat down the river and here I am. I thought about you when we passed your plantation. I mighty bad wanted to stop and see you. We left so fast the night we visited you that time—we were attacked and had to get away—but Mr. Offutt said no, we couldn't stop. How come you to be here, ma'am?"

"The plantation, it was too much for me, Abe." She sighed. "I'm an old woman and a lone one, and I could not handle the plantation any longer. So I sold it, Abe, and now my home is here in Royal Street, and I have Delphine and three others with me. Life may not be as exciting here, but neither is it so hard nor so lone. I like it. You like New Orleans, too, *n'est-ce pas?*"

Delphine came softly across the flagstones and set a tray on the little table. A polished silver coffeepot caught the curving reflection of the banana tree. The pot was steaming fragrantly and there were thin little cups and saucers, and some pretty small cakes.

Madame Duchesne poured Abe a cup of coffee and added sugar and milk. "Will you have a *brioche*, Abe? Seraphina makes delicious ones."

Abe never had heard of nor seen a *brioche* in his life—they didn't have 'em in cabins on the prairie—but since all he saw were the little cakes, he presumed they were *brioches*, and gingerly took one. It was good and he finished it off in two more bites.

"Have another, Abe." The old lady smiled. There was a peculiar contentment on her face, watching him eat. "It is so seldom that I have young people around me," she said, sighing a little once more. "Only Charlotte, who comes because of duty, I suppose, but at least she comes. Charlotte is sweet and very young, perhaps eighteen—I forget so easily nowadays—and so very much in love with life. But tell me what you've been doing, young man," she ordered in a different tone, delicately sipping her black coffee.

"Well, ma'am, we've seen a sight of things," he said, "and I'll be sorry to go. There's so much to see and do in New Orleans. Makes Illinois seem sort of dull and one-horse, doesn't it? Just think, I counted six newspaper offices here. Think of it, six! There aren't many more than that in all of the state of Illinois, I guess. I couldn't read what most of 'em printed, because a lot of it was French, I think. But it was nice to see them. Every time I bring a newspaper to our room, though, the rats chew it up, for a fact, ma'am!"

Madame shuddered. "Heavens, *cherie*, where do you have this room which is so full of rats?"

"Gallatin Street, ma'am. I know it isn't good, but it was cheap, and Jack and I didn't want to spend much. We make out, but I could do without the rats and the cockroaches and some of the smells. Ma'am, those cockroaches stand on the floor with their feet spraddled out and a-twirling their feelers, and they just dare you to stomp on them. Like as not they'll stare you down and sneer so you can't do it. For a fact!"

Madame Duchesne set down her coffee cup. She looked shaken. "*Mon enfant!*" she cried in horror. "We cannot let you live so low. Gallatin Street—it is the lowest of the low! No decent person lives there. Go now, at once, and get your things and come to my house. I am lonely, and you shall stay with me until you must go home again. Now—at once! Delphine! Show the gentleman to the gate and call Joseph to get out the carriage and take him to his lodging. And wait at the gate to let him in. He will not be long. Mr. Lincoln is to be our guest. Quickly now . . ."

Abe blinked. This was too fast for him.

"B-but ma'am," he stammered. "I'm not alone. My brother, Jack, is with me, and Mr. Offutt—though he's got a room by himself. But Jack and I—well, ma'am, I couldn't desert him. I promised Mother to look after him. And my goodness, ma'am, I plum forgot to get the powders for Jack! Some of the food he ate disagreed with him and he's laid up with a stomach ache. I've got to get some for him. Can you tell me where I'd find an English-speaking druggist?"

"*Non!*" she snapped. "I will give you powders for your brother. You shall bring him here and I will nurse him. But not Mr. Offutt. He will remain where he is. Go now with Joseph." She shook her head and clicked her tongue. Gallatin Street—to think of it!

Abe found himself in the carriage with Joseph before he knew what was happening. Joseph was stout and very black, and had more dignity than Abe felt comfortable with. They drove past the Market and down to dismal, ugly, odorous Gallatin Street, where Joseph showed his disapproval of the neighborhood by elevating his glossy black nose and refusing to look anywhere but straight ahead.

Abe went up the creaking stairs two at a time and found Jack feeling better, and explained matters to him. They shook the cockroaches out of their extra pairs of socks, gathered up their few belongings, told Madame Ambrose they were leaving, and went to the carriage. Joseph, in silent disdain, drove back to Royal Street.

The room which Abe and Jack occupied at Madame Duchesne's house was high-ceilinged and large, with lacy white curtains at the windows and a huge black walnut bed carved with cupids and flowers and dressed with cool white linens, a canopy, and mosquito netting. The ewer and basin were decorated with flowers and cupids, too, and on the whole Abe felt quite surrounded by the pink little dears.

But the elegance and comfort were amazing. Jack had never seen anything like that house, nor the efficient slaves who actually seemed to enjoy working for Madame Duchesne. And the food! Under Seraphina's ministrations in the kitchen, his stomach distress soon went away. He had a wonderful time. He had plenty of hot water for shaving and bathing, his clothes were kept pressed and clean for him; he could be neat and spruce and nobody laughed at him.

Abe was enjoying himself, too. Seraphina was solicitous about him. The tow-headed, rather stout Jack Johnston looked well fed, but not Abe.

"If'n you gwine to stay long enough, Mistah Lincoln," she protested, "maybe I git some flesh on dem bones o' yo's. Might git you fatted up so's you kin cast a shadder!" When Abe's kindly eyes smiled at her, Seraphina felt good through and through. She piled more shrimp and rice on his plate, or filled his bowl with more gumbo, or insisted he take another piece of pecan pie.

CHAPTER TWENTY NINE

Aʙᴇ ʜᴇᴀʀᴅ the light laughter one afternoon from where he
was reading in Madame Duchesne's library. He had found untold
wealth on those shelves—he never had had access to so many
books before and was in despair over the impossibility of reading
them all before the time came to go back to Illinois. Madame
Duchesne had tried to persuade him to stay longer in New
Orleans, but he knew Denton Offutt was going back in a few
days and he was obliged to go with him. Abe had promised to
clerk in that store in New Salem, and he never went back on
his promises.

"I got an obligation to Mr. Offutt," he'd explained patiently.
"I promised I'd help him build his store at New Salem and clerk
for him there. Besides, Jack's getting homesick."

"No, you could not go back on your word, not you," Madame
Duchesne had replied in a tired voice. "You would return to the
hardships and the squalor and the heartbreak of that barbaric
prairie country, when you could stay here and become a gentleman in New Orleans!"

Abe felt embarrassed. Sometimes he felt smothered in the old
lady's generosity and wished he was back in the rough, tough
backwoods country which he understood better than some of the

things she was trying to say to him. "I'd like to stay, ma'am, I would, for a fact. But I just can't." The matter had dropped, and he was trying to cram as many books into his time as he could.

Now at the sound of laughter, young laughter, that warm afternoon, he laid down his book and listened. Where had he heard that laugh before?

Madame Duchesne called to him. He put a marker in the book and went to the walled garden. A lovely young lady in pale yellow was taking coffee with the old lady. Abe saw a young thing with jet black curls and pale magnolia-white skin, and red lips curving deliciously over some joke she was telling the old lady. And then Abe knew.

Madame Duchesne looked up and saw his tall figure standing near the banana tree.

"Abe," she called in her clear voice. "Come, Charlotte, *cherie*, this is my Abe. He is a greater gentleman than you may think!"

The girl called Charlotte coolly looked him over with a lightning flick of her big, long-lashed, dark eyes. Abe, in his poor, ill-fitting clothes, felt catalogued and put in his place, not maliciously, but with finality.

"*Comme-çe va, M'sieu Abe?*" she smiled briefly and remotely at him, then turned her attention to the little black monkey.

"Howdy, ma'am," he said lamely, and the hand he had put out dropped to his side. She hadn't even seen it, she was so busy with that monkey. So she was like that . . .

"Come now," reproved Madame Duchesne. "Charlotte is being a snob and Abe is being *gauche*. Neither is like that, really. Abe, sit down. Charlotte, tell us, please, of the party you attended last night. It is almost too warm for parties, is it not?"

"Oh, but no, *Grand'mère!*" Charlotte protested. "But not yet —and this was such fun, and the gentlemen were so gallant! I danced every dance and didn't come away home till three. *Maman* was furious, but what could she do? *Tante* Marie was with me all the time!"

"Your gown—what did you wear? Tell us all," urged Madame Duchesne eagerly, as if she relived her own girlhood in the telling. Abe wished he was back with his book.

"Oh—an old thing—my thin white silk with the lace mantilla."

Abe looked up. "Did you wear red roses with it again this time, ma'am?" he asked innocently, and looked down at his knobby hands. There was a quirk around his lips.

Charlotte closed her mouth on the words she was about to say and just stared at the rough "Kaintuck" from the barbaric North. Madame Duchesne looked scarcely less taken aback.

Abe still examined his hands. Charlotte found her voice.

"M'sieu, did I hear you say—'Did I wear red roses, *again*'?— But how did you know—I have never, never seen you before in my life?" Her voice carried the conviction that gave Abe the idea she never wanted to see him again, either.

"Yes, ma'am, that's what I said. You see, I saw you that night —I caught the rose you threw to me. It was a mighty pretty flower. I was sorry when it faded."

"And what is this, if you please? Charlotte throwing roses at my Abe, and he catches them—and does he wear this rose next his heart?" cried Madame Duchesne in great delight.

"It was only a jest, *Grand'mère*," the girl protested, coloring most becomingly, Abe observed with interest. He was secretly pleased that he'd caught her so that she acted natural. "It was at Eugenie LeMonnier's *petit bal*. Georges Livaudais dared me to throw a rose to the first gentleman who passed below on the street—he said I would not dare. But I did—there were two who were just passing—I could not see them well, but I threw the rose and ran back inside." And she looked just a mite flattered that he'd caught it, Abe deducted.

Charlotte did not stay very long. She seemed ill at ease under Abe's quizzical gaze, and made her farewells quickly. When she had gone, Madame Duchesne turned to Abe.

"You have caught her fancy, Abe," she said soberly. "Perhaps, after all, it is better that you go home soon."

"But, ma'am, she hates the sight of me!" protested Abe. "There never was an uglier face than mine—I'm all lanky bones and dressed poorly. I don't talk right and I don't act right. *She* doesn't fancy me, not her. But I did get under her skin, didn't I, ma'am, and I don't regret it!" Smiling to himself, Abe went back to his book.

All that week, for one reason or another, Charlotte was in and out. Sometimes with studied indifference she ignored Abe— she never could even see Jack, who tried his best to flirt with her but met cold discouragement at every attempt. Sometimes she asked Abe's opinion on some matter and hung on his words with a most flattering attention. Sometimes she openly flirted with him, and then again he was ignored as if she could see through him, as if he wasn't there at all.

Abe was mightily confused. He didn't know whether to be friendly and talk when she wanted him to talk, or just to retire somewhere when he heard those light footsteps in the passage and that silvery voice in the walled garden.

"Don't let the child turn your head, Abe," Madame Duchesne finally warned him. "She isn't for you and your good sense knows it—but don't lose that good sense. Charlotte will become the wife of Hippolyte de Martineau next October. Until then she plays at flirting with every man she sees, even you, my poor

DENTON OFFUTT AT ONCE BECAME THE MAN OF BUSINESS. HE BRUSHED HIS
BEST COAT, BUFFED HIS HAT, SHINED HIS BOOTS AND BUSTLED OFF

A MONTH IN THE OLD CITY WHICH WAS NEW ORLEANS IN 1831 COULD
HARDLY BE DULL TO ABE AND JACK, SALLYING OUT TO EXPLORE

Abe. She would even flirt with your dull Jack if he were not quite so dull. When do you go home, Abe?"

He felt a little empty inside. The small, sweet feeling he had let grow for Charlotte suddenly was very dead.

"I saw Mr. Offutt yesterday and he says we sail on the eighteenth, ma'am. Three days from now. Yes, I guess it's just as well, maybe better. I see what you mean. I guess I just never saw a girl like her before."

"No, you never did." The old lady smiled whimsically at him. "That kind—I think they are only to be found in *Nouvelle Orléans!*"

CHAPTER THIRTY

ON THE DAY before they were to depart from New Orleans, Jack and Abe ran into a crowd gathered around a low, odorous, open market on a street they had missed before. They pushed closer to see what was going on, and the sight that met their eyes set the two back on their heels. No one else, however, seemed at all disturbed, but obviously were enjoying the proceedings. It was the slave market and a sale was in progress.

A young Negress, half-clothed, stood quietly as the auctioneer pointed out her merits, while men in elegant white cravats and gloves, tall hats, and tail coats stood about, bidding higher and higher. Sold, sold, to the gentleman from Bayou St. John.

The next batch of slaves stepped up on the blocks and the sale went on. Abe, petrified with his own distaste, watched as if he were hypnotized. He didn't want to stay, yet he could not make himself go away.

And then Abraham Lincoln, without realizing that he was crying, felt tears running down his thin cheeks, for there beside one of the blocks, waiting to be put up for sale, was Caleb—his friend, Caleb. Near him was a finely-boned young woman with pale cocoa-colored skin and straight hair fastened neatly at the back of her head. A little boy, wide-eyed, clung tightly to her hand and looked out at the crowd, but the woman's eyes were fixed in an interlocking gaze, like an embrace, upon Caleb's tragic face.

Bidding began on the other six slaves who, with Caleb and his family, went up for sale at the same time. Abe's blood chilled at the stark awfulness of what he was seeing and of what he was about to see when Caleb and Celine and little Cal once more were torn apart.

He wormed his way through the crowd and pushed up as close as he could to the place where the chained slaves waited to be sold.

"Caleb," he called softly. "Caleb, it's Abe Lincoln. Howdy, boy!"

Caleb started. His hands went out in front of him, then, heavy with their chains, they dropped to his sides. He looked up into Abe's pitying eyes.

"Mistah Lincoln!" he whispered. "I found 'em. I found Celine and little Cal!"

"But Caleb—what happened? How come—this?"

"My masta, he caught up with me in Nashville," he said sadly, "and Celine, she carried on so, he finally sold me to her masta, who was a very kind man, Mistah Lincoln. But three days aftah we been together, he died sudden—oh, it was turrible, Mistah Lincoln. And we was sold down the rivah, aftah all. I nevah thought to be sold in Newerleans, but nothin' mattahs if only Celine and little Cal are sold with me. If they ain't—if they ain't—" He bent over quickly to whisper, "A voodoo woman give me some poison. If Celine and me is separated, we goin' to take the poison. That way we'll be togethah in de Lawd. I know He undahstan'."

"No, Caleb, *no!*" cried Abe in horror, feeling his stomach turn over inside him at the thought. "That isn't right!"

"I know it ain't, Mistah Lincoln. It's only fo' de last hope, when ev'ything else gone. But we prayin' now, me and Celine, and little Cal is, too, best he knows. And Jesus say, if any two or three are gathered togethah in His name, he answer dey prayers." Caleb's eyes held deep faith.

"Caleb," Abe said suddenly. "Hold on. Don't do anything rash. Just keep on praying. I'll be back!" He shoved blindly out of the crowd and past Jack Johnston. Then, with his long legs covering the sidewalks in great strides, he ran back to Royal Street. He pounded on the gate until Delphine let him in.

"Where's Madame Duchesne?" he gasped. "I got to see her quick!"

"In de garden, suh," Delphine said placidly. Nothing ever startled Delphine.

He raced to the peaceful, cool, walled garden which seemed a million miles away from the heat, smells, and horror of the slave market. Madame Duchesne was reading *L'Abielle*, her favorite newspaper. She looked up as Abe clattered across the flagstones.

"Abe, what in the name of Heaven?"

"Ma'am, listen to me. They're selling a friend of mine at the slave market. I've got to save him, him and Celine and little Cal, and I don't know how to do it. They're slaves, ma'am, and they're fine people. Caleb rode a ways on our boat and we vowed not to tell, but I've got to tell you. And if they sell him and Celine to different folks, they'll kill themselves. They've got voodoo poison! What can we do?"

Breathing heavily, the tears starting helplessly out of his eyes again, he dropped into one of the uncomfortable iron chairs.

Madame Duchesne, with precise fingers, creased her newspaper neatly in four sections.

"Call Joseph, if you please, Delphine, and bring my shawl and bonnet. I am going out. Come, Abe," said Madame Duchesne as calmly as if she contemplated a visit to the fruit stall.

In the carriage, they clattered over the ruts to the slave market. Abe was speechless. Madame Duchesne preserved an unruffled and unapproachable silence.

They found Caleb just put up for bidding. Abe looked quickly for Celine and little Cal, and found them on another block. Celine looked ready to collapse and her big eyes were wide with dreadful fear.

"What am I offered for this fine buck, aged twenty-three, sound in wind and limb, fit for a house servant, trained to wait on gentlemen? What am I bid?"

Madame Duchesne stood up in her carriage and her voice rose more strongly than Abe would have believed possible above all that crowd.

"Fifteen hundred dollars for the man, if his wife and child come with him," she said.

There was a murmur. "I bid sixteen hundred," said a man's voice in the front of the crowd. Abe's heart was thudding against his ribs so hard he was sure Madame Duchesne could hear it. She was still on her feet. Abe in his nervousness climbed out and stood beside the carriage.

"Sixteen hundred and fifty," said her quiet voice.

"Seventeen hundred," said the man.

"Seventeen hundred and fifty," said Madame.

"Seventeen hundred and seventy-five," cried the man impatiently.

"Seventeen-eighty," came Madame Duchesne's calm voice.

"Eighteen hundred!" the man snapped angrily. "They're not

worth more than that, lady," he shouted above the crowd. "I bid eighteen hundred and not a picayune more!"

"Eighteen hundred dollars, eighteen hundred dollars," called the auctioneer. "Will the lady go higher, will the lady go higher? Eighteen hundred, eighteen hundred for three fine slaves. Going, going, at eighteen hundred to the gentleman—where are you from, sir?—to the gentleman from Bayou LaFourche. Does the lady bid more? Going—"

Abe held his breath. Would she, could she, bid any higher? He still had twenty dollars left from what Denton Offutt had paid him for building and piloting the flatboat. He dug into his pocket and put the money in her hand, every bit he had, all but some small change. She looked quickly down at it, and up at him, smiled—

"I bid eighteen hundred and twenty dollars," she said clearly.

"Sold, sold, sold, sold to the lady for eighteen hundred and twenty dollars!" Abe took a wonderful, chest-filling, deep breath as the gavel dropped. "Your name, Madame?"

"Madame Henri Duchesne, 698 Royal Street. You may send them along at once and call for the money and bill of sale at my residence. Come Abe, come Joseph."

Abe climbed in with the magnificent old lady.

"Thank you, ma'am," he said simply. "I'll never forget this as long as I live. That was a mighty wonderful thing for you to do. You're a great lady, ma'am, if I may make so bold as to say so."

"You may," she said drily. "And I suppose that was all the money you possess in the world?" she added casually.

"Yes, but that doesn't matter. I can always earn more."

"Abe," she went on, "I have no slaves. I set them all free when I sold the plantation. Delphine and Joseph and Seraphina and Jacob are free and they work for me as paid servants. Caleb and his wife and child are free now, too, and little Cal will grow up as a free man. I couldn't go to my grave knowing I'd bought and sold human flesh and left them in bondage."

Abe looked at her with a deeper respect and admiration than he'd had for any woman, except for his stepmother, Sarah Lincoln.

As the carriage moved slowly through the crowd, it passed Jack Johnston, who still hadn't comprehended just what had happened. But he heard Abe say, "Ma'am, you're right! If I ever had a chance to hit at slavery, I'd hit it hard!"

CHAPTER THIRTY ONE

"MA'AM, WHAT could I get to take home to my mother? She'd be mighty proud if I brought her something, but I wish to land I knew what to get. I haven't much to spend, either, and that's a fact." He had given all but his small change to help buy Caleb and his family, and although Madame Duchesne had tried to return the money to him, he hotly refused. He insisted he could earn all he needed by working on the docks.

Now he was in the garden where a wisteria vine climbing over the wall dripped the last of its purple blossoms into the fountain and at the feet of the little white Virgin in the niche. The black monkey sat on Madame Duchesne's shoulder; the macaw still dropped pebbles into the pool.

"A bit of jewelry, perhaps," said Madame Duchesne, lazily. "All women like jewelry. Has she much?"

"Much? Why, ma'am, she hasn't any, except a brass breastpin with a goldstone set. She always liked that, but she never had anything else. Cabin folks don't have much chance to wear jewelry, nor get it, either!" He laughed shortly, remembering his stepmother bending her back over a wash tub, sweeping the floor, trying to chink up the window cracks so the cold air wouldn't come in so badly; his stepmother making soap and weaving homespun cloth, doing all the hard chores which meant living in a prairie cabin. How could he make a woman of luxury like Madame Duchesne see the life his stepmother led? Sarah Lincoln deserved something pretty to look at and sometimes to pin on her dress when the work was done. He'd do his best to see she didn't always have to work so hard.

Madame Duchesne, studying Abe's face, put away her lazy look and her lazy voice. She called briskly to Delphine.

"Delphine, bring me my small jewel case, the one with the red velvet cover."

Delphine brought it and put it into the old lady's blue-veined hands. Madame opened the snap catch and laid back the lid, and took out something which she looked at for a long moment. Then she placed it in Abe's hand.

"Here is something to take to your mother," she said softly. "It is a pin which belonged to my own mother, long ago in France. Take it to your mother with the blessing of a lone woman who borrowed her son for a little while and found him a tonic to her soul."

Abe couldn't say anything. He swallowed hard. Finally he managed, "Ma'am, I shouldn't take anything so valuable. But I do think you really want me to, and I know my mother will be mighty obliged to you. She loves pretty things. She can wear this on her best dress when the circuit rider comes around. I do thank you kindly, ma'am!" Abe in wonder examined the little gold breastpin with its old-fashioned coral sets and the tiny seed pearls arranged in circlets around them. Sarah Lincoln would love it and cherish it forever.

Tomorrow, if he could find a way to pay for his passage, Abe would start home. Home? Where was home? In his mind a change had taken place since he had started in a cottonwood canoe down the flooding Sangamon last March. Home had been so many places—Kentucky, Indiana, Illinois—and now his parents, discouraged with the Decatur cabin after the dreadful winter just passed, by this time would have moved south to Coles County. Very likely Tom Lincoln would have built himself another cabin that would be like all the rest.

But to Abe that was not home, not any more. Suddenly—though it had been growing in him during the three months he had been away—suddenly he knew he was a man. He was on his own. Neither the Decatur cabin nor the Coles County cabin ever would be home to him. He was going back to New Salem with Denton Offutt. Now, wherever Abe was, there was his home. In a way, it was a queer, lost sort of sensation; but, in another way, it made him feel he was indeed a man grown. This voyage had done that to him.

CHAPTER THIRTY TWO

Abe's pockets held very little to show for three months of work and adventure. If he was to pay his passage on the steamboat and take any money home to his parents, he would surely have to do some fast planning and working. Inside himself, he knew that his experiences of the past three months had been priceless, but to Tom Lincoln there had to be some evaluation in dollars. Tom would have plenty to say, none of it complimentary, if Abe came back with empty pockets.

That evening he went alone to the water front and found the captain of the *New Orleans Belle*.

"Captain, sir," Abe began at once, "I and my friends are sailing north with you tomorrow. They've got money for their passage, but I haven't. Have you got a job open in your crew? I know the Mississippi channel pretty fair; I've navigated it twice."

The captain's keen eyes looked at Abe. He asked a question or two, and pretty soon Abe had a job.

Next morning Denton Offutt and Jack Johnston met Abe, as they had planned ahead of time, on the *New Orleans Belle*, and found him a member of the steamboat's crew. He had bade farewell to Madame Duchesne, who wept a little afterward to lose him. He said good-bye to Caleb and Celine and little Cal, to Joseph and Jacob and Delphine, and to Seraphina, who cried into her apron to see him go. He had not seen Charlotte for several days. After all, it was just as well. And the little black monkey had chittered at him as Delphine took him for the last time through the two gates and out to the street. She shook his hand, and then on long legs he was off through the early morning mists of New Orleans. Jack had made his own farewells brief and to the point.

With a thrilling commotion of whistles blowing, bells ringing and steam sizzling, the big paddle wheels slowly began to turn and the great white steamboat moved in elegance away from the wharf. Majestically, the *New Orleans Belle* started north up the Mississippi.

As the steamboat pushed upstream, moving against the powerful current which brought flatboats down but never took them back again, Abe felt a glorious sensation of power. To him, this was the climax to the whole exciting journey down three rivers, south—this and the memory of the happy faces of Caleb and Celine and little Cal as he had left them in Madame Duchesne's sheltered garden.